· SCHOLASTIC SUCCESS WITH ·

1st GRADE
WORKBOOK

SCHOLASTIC
Teacher
RESOURCES

Editor: Ourania Papacharalambous
Cover design by Anna Christian; cover illustration by Rob McClurkan
Interior design by Cynthia Ng
Interior illustrations by Gabriele Antonini (56–99); Stephen Brown (17–18, 20, 23–24, 26–29, 34–35, 41, 43, 45, 48–50); Dan Crisp (236); Doug Jones (spot art); Maarten Lenoir (102–162); and Roger Simó (164–208)
Maps: Jim McMahon (217, 247–248, 251); Mapping Specialists, Ltd. (212, 216, 220–221, 223–225, 227–231, 234–235, 238, 240–241, 243–246, 250); Clive Scruton and Millicent Schaffer (map illustrations)

Photos ©: 27, 29 (icons): The Noun Project; 214, 226 (all): Scholastic Inc.; 257 (top): KeithSzafranski/Getty Images; 257 (center): Suhaimi Sulaiman/EyeEm/Getty Images; 257 (bottom): Rene Krekels/Minden Pictures; 257 (bottom inset): Derek Middleton/Minden Pictures; 260: Dannyphoto80/Dreamstime; 263: luamduan/Getty Images; 264 (left): Napat_Polchoke/Getty Images; 264 (right): AnetteAndersen/Getty Images; 265: NatalyaAksenova/Getty Images; 266: yamatao/Getty Images; 267: Top Photo Corporation/Getty Images; 269 (top): Sazonoff/Getty Images; 269 (bottom): toomler/Getty Images; 271: bigemrg/Getty Images; 272: Tsekhmister/Getty Images; 274 (left): IMNATURE/Getty Images; 274 (right): fotoco-istock/Getty Images; 276 (top): Pascale Gueret/Getty Images; 276 (bottom): McKayPhotography/Getty Images; 282: Jarenwicklund/Dreamstime; 285 (top): focussucof/Getty Images; 285 (center top): Louise Wightman/Getty Images; 285 (center bottom): bamas/Getty Images; 285 (bottom): JohnPitcher/Getty Images; 286 (top): by_adr/Getty Images; 286 (left): onairjiw/Getty Images; 286 (right): Chris Knorr/Design Pics/Getty Images; 287: Roger Tidman/Getty Images; 290: Nati Harnik/AP Images; 293: Ariel Skelley/Getty Images; 313: dontree_m/Getty Images; 321 (notes): The Noun Project; 215, 216: Scholastic Inc. All other photos © Shutterstock.com

TABLE OF CONTENTS

READING COMPREHENSION

Tim Can Read
(Understand the reading process) 12

Trucks (Find the main idea) 13

Acrobats (Find the main idea) 14

Your Name (Find the main idea) 15

Striped Critters (Read for details) 16

Ricky's Wish (Read for details) 17

Going to Grammy's (Read for details) 18

George W. Bush (Read for details) 19

Mr. Lee's Store (Real or fantasy?) 20

Cool Clouds (Real or fantasy?) 21

Fun at the Farm (Real or fantasy?) 22

Ready for School (Sequence events) 23

Swimming Lessons (Sequence events) 24

Shapes in the Sky (Follow directions) 25

My Monster (Follow directions) 26

Fun at the Beach (Follow directions) 27

My New Rug (Draw conclusions) 28

Polly Want a Cracker? (Draw conclusions) 29

You Be the Artist (Visualize) 30

A Stormy Day (Visualize) 31

Who Am I? (Make inferences) 32

What's Going On? (Make inferences) 33

Make a Cartoon (Make inferences) 34

Clean Your Room (Sort and classify) 35

Going to the Mall (Sort and classify) 36

My Favorites (Sort and classify) 37

Ouch! (Make predictions) 38

What Will Sam Do? (Make predictions) 39

Riddle Fun (Compare and contrast) 40

Twins (Compare and contrast) 41

Soldier Moms (Compare and contrast) 42

Dinosaur Clues (Develop vocabulary) 43

Amazing Animal Facts
(Develop vocabulary) 44

A Tiny Town (Develop vocabulary) 45

Oops! (Identify cause and effect) 46

Wanda Wiggleworm
(Identify cause and effect) 47

School Rules (Identify cause and effect) 48

Mixed-Up Margie (Analyze characters) 49

Miss Ticklefoot (Analyze characters) 50

Different Friends (Analyze characters) 51

Poetry (Appreciate literature) 52

A Fable (Appreciate literature) 53

Library Books (Appreciate literature) 54

HANDWRITING

Aa 56

Bb 57

Cc 58

Dd 59

Ee 60

Ff 61

Gg 62

Hh	63
Ii	64
Jj	65
Kk	66
Ll	67
Mm	68
Nn	69
Oo	70
Pp	71
Qq	72
Rr	73
Ss	74
Tt	75
Uu	76
Vv	77
Ww	78
Xx	79
Yy	80
Zz	81
A–Z	82
a–z	83
1–5	84
6–10	85
Color Words	86
More Color Words	87
Number Words	88
More Number Words	89
Shapes	90
Days of the Week	91
Months	92
Special Days	94
Animals From A to Z	96
The Continents	98
The Planets	99
Keep Up the Good Work!	100

GRAMMAR

Capitalizing First Word	102
Periods	105
Capitalizing I	108
Simple Sentences	111
Word Order	114
Question Sentences	117
Naming Words	120
Capitalizing Special Names	123
Action Words	126
Describing Words	129
Telling Sentences	132
Exclamation Sentences	135
Punctuation Power	138
Singular/Plural Nouns	139
Action Words (Part 2)	142
Naming Words (Part 2)	145
Word Order (Part 2)	148
Capitalizing Titles	151
Naming Words (Part 3)	154
Linking Verbs	157
Capitalizing Names	160
Capitalizing Names and First Words	161

WRITING

That's Amazing! (Recognize capital letters) 164

Squeak! (Capitalize sentence beginnings) 165

Counting Sheep
(Capitalize sentence beginnings) 166

Sweet Dreams!
(Capitalize sentence beginnings) 167

The Night Sky (Recognize periods) 168

Twinkle, Twinkle, Little Star
(Punctuate statements) 169

Hop to It!
(Capitalize/punctuate statements) 170

Hop to It Some More!
(Capitalize/punctuate statements) 171

Striped Sentences (Identify a sentence) 172

High-Flying Sentences
(Identify a sentence) 173

At the Seashore (Sequence a sentence) 174

In the Rain Forest (Sequence a story) 175

Snakes Alive!
(Parts of a sentence: Naming part) 176

Slithering Sentences
(Parts of a sentence: Naming part) 177

Who Is That?
(Parts of a sentence: Naming part) 178

Where Is That?
(Parts of a sentence: Naming part) 179

Vacation Photos (Write a sentence) 180

More Vacation Photos (Write a sentence) 181

No Bones About It!
(Parts of a sentence: Identify the action) 182

Mighty Good Sentences
(Parts of a sentence: Complete the action) 183

A Busy Classroom
(Parts of a sentence: Write the verb) 184

Pencil It In
(Parts of a sentence: Determine the verb) 185

Topsy-Turvy! (Write sentences) 186

What Is Going On? (Write sentences) 187

The Caboose (Understand sentence parts) 188

When Was That? (Identify sentence parts) 189

Chugging Along
(Understand sentence parts) 190

My Busy Day (Complete a sentence) 191

Silly Sentences (Write 3-part sentences) 192

Sweet Sentences (Write 3-part sentences) 193

Home Sweet Home (Write 3-part sentences) 194

The Construction Crew
(Write 3-part sentences) 195

Mystery Boxes (Explore adjectives) 196

Sensational Words (Add adjectives) 197

More Describing Words (Adjectives) 198

Pretty Packages (Brainstorm adjectives) 199

What's Inside?
(Complete describing sentences) 200

A Walk in the Park (Write adjectives) 201

Around Town (Write descriptive sentences) 202

Keep It in Order
(Complete a sequenced story) 203

What's Next? (Write sequenced directions) 204

Which Title Fits? (Name a story) 205

A Terrific Title
(Parts of a story: Write the title) 206

Story Strips (Parts of a story:
Write the beginning, middle, and end) 207

More Story Strips
(Parts of a story: Retell a 3-part story) 208

MAPS

What Is a Map? 210

Make a Map 212

A Picture of Earth 214

What Is a Globe? 215

Maps and Globes 216

Big and Small Places 218

Near or Far? 220

Left or Right? 222

Four Main Directions 224

What Are Map Symbols? 226

Use Map Symbols 228

A Neighborhood Map 230

Follow the Treasure! 232

Treasure Map 234

Let's Visit the Sea Park 235

Land and Water 236

Land and Water on a Map 238

Our World 240

Our Continent 242

The United States 244

State Maps.. 246

A City Map 248

Map Review 250

Thinking About Maps...................................252

Glossary..253

SCIENCE

Beautiful Babies (Animal babies) 256

Babies Change and Grow! (Animal babies) 257

All Kinds of Animals (Animals) 262

A Home for Koalas (Needs of living things) 263

Inspect the Insects (Insects) 268

Way to 'Bee' Helpful! (Pollinators) 269

Which Insect Is It? (Compare insects) 274

Auks and Hawks (Birds) 276

Name That Dinosaur (Dinosaurs) 278

Plants We Eat (Nutrition) 279

Thumbs Up! (Human body) 280

Ahh... choo! (Health) 282

The Four Seasons (Seasons) 284

The Changing Seasons (Seasons) 285

High Waters (Weather) 290

Weather Watchers (Weather vocabulary) 292

Powerful Push (Wind power) 293

Fanciful Flowers (Flowers) 298

Out of This World (Space) 299

What's on Mars? (Space) 300

MATH

Funny Dog (Add to 10) 302

Lovely Ladybugs (Add to 10) 303

Beautiful Bouquets
(Add to 10/even and odd numbers) 304

Snowflake Math (Add to 10) 305

Diamond Works (Subtract from 10) 306

Juggling Act (Subtract from 10) 307

Ocean Life (Subtract from 10) 308

Trucking Along (Subtract from 10) 310

Night Lights (Subtract from 10) 311

Hop to It: Add and Subtract
(Add/subtract through 10) 312

Kickboard Matchup
(Add/subtract through 10) 313

Blast Off (Add/subtract through 10) 314

Out on the Town (Add/subtract
through 10—bar graph) 315

Shapes on a Snake
(Add/subtract through 10) 316

Planes... Trains... *(Add/subtract through 10—problem solving)* 317

Slice It Up *(Add to 18)* 318

Leap on Over *(Add to 18)* 319

Gumball, Anyone? *(Add to 18)* 320

Key Code *(Add to 18)* 321

Flying High *(Add to 18)* 322

Double Dips *(Add to 18—doubles)* 323

Not Far From Home *(Add to 18—doubles)* 324

Break the Code *(Subtract from 18)* 325

The Big Search *(Subtract from 18)* 326

Race Through the Facts
(Add/subtract through 18) 327

Little Snacks
(Add/subtract through 18) 328

Flying Families *(Add/subtract through 18—fact families)* 329

Colorful Flowers *(Add/subtract through 18—bar graph)* 330

A Nutty Bunch
(Add/subtract through 18) 331

Penguin Parade
(Add/subtract through 18) 332

A Perfect Strike *(Add/subtract through 18—three addends)* 333

What a Treat! *(Add/subtract through 18—problem solving)* 334

Have a Heart *(Group tens and ones)* 335

So Many Flowers!
(Place value: tens and ones) 336

Counting Blocks
(Place value: tens and ones) 337

Beautiful Butterflies
(Add 2-digit and 1-digit numbers) 338

Where's the Beach?
(Add 2-digit and 1-digit numbers) 339

By the Seashore
(Add 2-digit and 1-digit numbers) 340

Sail Away
(Add 2-digit and 1-digit numbers) 341

Dino-Math
(Subtract 1-digit from 2-digit numbers) 342

Butterfly Friends
(Subtract 1-digit from 2-digit numbers) 343

Treasure Island
(Subtract 1-digit from 2-digit numbers) 344

Riding on Air *(Add 2-digit numbers)* 345

Star Math *(Add 2-digit numbers)* 346

Sunflower Math
(Add 2-digit numbers) 347

Ten-Point Star *(Add 2-digit numbers)* ...348

Designer Diamond *(Add 2-digit numbers)* 349

Color the Bow
(Subtract 2-digit numbers) 350

Have a Ball *(Subtract 2-digit numbers)* 351

Amazing Maze
(Subtract 2-digit numbers) 352

Opposites Attract
(Add/subtract 2-digit numbers) 353

How Much Money?
(Add/subtract 2-digit numbers, money) 354

Going to Market
(Add/subtract 2-digit numbers, money) 355

Snuggle Up With a Book
(Add/subtract 2-digit numbers) 356

Let the Sun Shine
(Add/subtract 2-digit numbers) 357

Animal Surprises
(Add/subtract 2-digit numbers) 358

Fishbowl Families
(Add/subtract 2-digit numbers) 359

All Kinds of Patterns! (Patterns) 360

More Patterns (Patterns, number sense) 361

Picking Out Patterns
(Patterns, number sense) 362

Odd and Even Patterns
(Odd and even numbers, patterns) 363

Odds or Evens? (Even and odd numbers) 364

Dancing Bear (Count) 365

Snowflakes on Mittens (Skip counting) 366

Snail Mail (Skip count by twos) 367

Patterns of Five (Skip count by fives) 368

I Can Skip Count! (Skip count by 10s) 369

Sign Shape (Recognize shapes) 370

Bird Feeder Geometry (Recognize shapes) 371

Corners and Sides (Understand shapes) 372

Shape Study (Symmetry) 373

Equal Halves? (Symmetry) 374

Give Us Symmetry! (Symmetry) 375

Pattern Block Design
(Addition equations, patterns) 376

Time to Get Up! (Story problems) 377

Money Matters
(Count coins/value) 378

That's the Tooth!
(Count coins/value) 379

Measuring Up (Measure length) 380

Penguin Family on Parade
(Measure height, compare) 381

Look and Learn
(Estimate, measure length) 382

Turn Up the Volume (Measure volume) 383

Adding Sides (Measure length) 384

Centimeters (Measure length) 385

Five Senses (Use a graph) 386

Rainbow Graph (Use a graph) 387

Fruits and Vegetables
(Ordered pairs and coordinates) 388

Starry Night (Graph coordinates) 389

December Weather (Read tables) 390

Fun With Fractions (Identify equal parts) 391

Parts to Color (Simple fractions) 392

More Parts to Color (Simple fractions) 393

Clock Work (Tell time) 394

More Clock Work (Estimate time) 395

Even More Clock Work (Tell time) 396

About Time (Tell time) 397

Balloon Clocks (Tell time) 398

Answer Key 399

All About Me 417–432

Flash Cards 433–440

Stickers 441

"Nothing succeeds like success."

Alexandre Dumas the Elder, 1854

Dear Family:

Congratulations on choosing this wonderful resource for your child. For more than a century, Scholastic has been a leader in educational publishing, creating quality materials for use in schools and at home.

As a partner in your child's academic success, you'll want to get the most out of the learning experience offered in this book. To help your child learn at home, try following these helpful hints:

★ Provide a comfortable and quiet place to work.

★ Make sure your child has all the supplies he or she needs, such as pencils, crayons, or markers.

★ Enjoy frequent work sessions, but keep them short. Ten to 15 minutes is an ideal length of time for a child in the first grade.

★ Praise your child's successes and encourage his or her efforts. Offer positive support when your child needs extra help.

★ Display your child's work and share his or her progress with family and friends.

After page 416, you'll find additional sections for your child to complete:

★ The *All About Me* booklet on pages 417–432 can be removed and stapled to become a special keepsake you'll treasure for years to come.

★ The flash cards in the back of the book feature the top sight words children need to know. The flash cards are a fun way to learn the most frequently used words in reading and writing.

Take the lead and help your child succeed with *Scholastic Success With 1st Grade Workbook!*

FOCUS SKILLS

The activities in this workbook reinforce age-appropriate skills and will help your child meet the following standards established as goals by leading educators.

Mathematics

★ Uses a variety of strategies when problem-solving

★ Understands and applies number concepts

★ Uses basic and advanced procedures while performing computation

★ Understands and applies concepts of measurement

★ Understands and applies concepts of geometry

Writing

★ Understands and uses the writing process

★ Uses grammatical and mechanical conventions in written compositions

Reading

★ Understands and uses the general skills and strategies of the reading process

★ Can read and understand a variety of literary texts

★ Can understand and interpret a variety of informational texts

Geography

★ Understands the characteristics and uses of maps and globes

★ Knows the location of places, geographic features, and patterns of the environment

Science

★ Plans and carries out investigations to answer questions or test solutions

★ Analyzes animals and insects, and how they interact with their environment

★ Identifies plants and their parts, and recognizes some as a food source

★ Understands the human body

★ Recognizes weather and seasonal patterns

★ Analyzes forces and motion

READING COMPREHENSION

Tim Can Read

Tim is a good reader. He uses clues to help him read. First, he looks at the picture. That helps him know what the story is about. Next, he reads the title of the story. Now he knows a little more. As he reads the story, the words make pictures in his mind.

Color in the book beside the correct answer.

1 Who is Tim?

☐ a good reader   ☐ a math whiz

2 What does Tim do first?

☐ reads the story   ☐ looks at the picture

3 What else helps Tim know what the story will be about?

☐ the title   ☐ the page number

4 As he reads, what makes pictures in Tim's mind?

☐ the letters   ☐ the words

☆ Try reading the stories in this book the way that Tim does. If you do, you will be a good reader, too! Write the name of your favorite book here:

_____

Trucks

**Read about trucks.
Then follow the directions below.**

The **main idea** tells us what the whole story is about.

Trucks do important work. Dump trucks carry away sand and rocks. Cement trucks have a barrel that turns round and round. They deliver cement to workers who are making sidewalks. Fire trucks carry water hoses and firefighters. Gasoline is delivered in large tank trucks. Flat bed trucks carry wood to people who are building houses.

1 What is the main idea of the paragraph? Write it in the circle below.

2 Draw a line from the main idea to the trucks described in the paragraph.

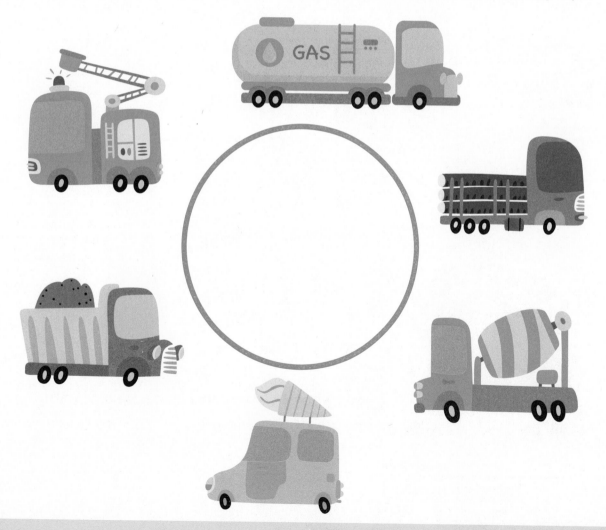

Acrobats

Today I went to the county fair. My favorite part of the fair was the acrobats. Acrobats can do great things. An acrobat named Priscilla turned flips while walking on a wire high in the air. The Amazing Ricardo juggled clubs while riding a unicycle. At the end of the show, about twelve acrobats created a human pyramid.

Color in the flag that tells the main idea.

Clowns drive tiny cars.

Balloons can be shaped like animals.

Pinky rides a horse.

Acrobats can do great things.

Fancy Pants sang a song.

Your Name

When you were born, your parents thought of a name for you. You might be named after someone in the family. Maybe you were named after a movie star! Almost every name has a meaning. *Pamela* means "honey." *Nick* means "victory of the people." *Ellen* means "bright." Sometimes books about baby names tell the meanings. Many of the meanings will surprise you!

Circle the name below that has the main idea of the text in it.

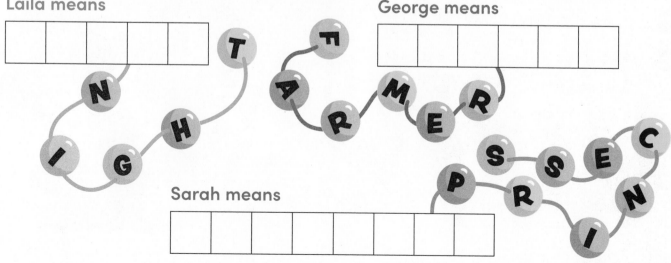

To find out the meanings of the names in the puzzle below, follow each string of beads. Copy the letters on each bead in order in the boxes.

Laila means

George means

Sarah means

Striped Critters

Skunks are small animals that live in the woods. They have black fur with one or two white stripes down their backs. Bugs are their favorite food. They also eat mice. If a skunk raises its tail, run away! Skunks can spray a very smelly liquid at anyone who bothers them.

Details are parts of a story. Details help you understand what the text is about.

Write the answers in the crossword puzzle.

Across:

2 What color are the stripes on a skunk's fur?

5 What is a skunk's favorite food?

Down:

1 What is another thing that skunks like to eat?

2 Where do skunks live?

3 What does a skunk raise when it is getting ready to spray?

4 What should you do if a skunk raises its tail?

Ricky's Wish

Ricky loved to go camping. One day during reading class, he began to daydream about camping in the mountains. He thought about going fishing and riding horses. It would be fun to gather logs to build a campfire and cook hot dogs. He and his dad could set up the tent near some big trees. He wishes he were in his canoe right now. Just then, Ricky heard his teacher say, "Ricky, it is your turn to read." Oh, no! He had lost the place!

Circle these things from the text in the picture below: a fish, a fishing pole, a log for campfire, a hot dog, a tree, and a canoe.

1 Where was Ricky during this story? _____

_____

2 Where would Ricky like to have been? _____

_____

Going to Grammy's

Kelly is going to spend the night with her grandmother. She will need to take her pajamas, a shirt, and some shorts. Into the suitcase go her toothbrush, toothpaste, and hairbrush. Grammy told her to bring a swimsuit in case it was warm enough to swim. Mom said to pack her favorite pillow and storybooks. Dad said, "Don't forget to take Grammy's sunglasses that she left here last week." Now Kelly is ready to go!

1 Color the things that Kelly packed in her suitcase.

2 A compound word is a big word that is made up of two little words. For example, cow + boy = cowboy. Find 8 compound words in this story and circle them.

⭐ On another sheet of paper, make a list of things you would pack if you were going to spend the night at your grandmother's house.

George W. Bush

George W. Bush grew up in Texas. When he finished college, he worked in the oil business. Later on, he became the governor of Texas, then the 43rd president of the United States. His wife's name is Laura. They have twin daughters named Jenna and Barbara. The Bush family owns a ranch in Texas. They had two dogs named Barney and Spotty.

The Bush family also had a cat. To find out the name of their cat, write the answers in the blanks. Then copy the letters that are in the shapes into the empty shapes below.

1 Mr. Bush grew up in ____ ____ ____ ⬡ ____.

2 He worked in the ____ △____ business.

3 He became the 43rd ____ ____ ____ ____ ⬓ ____ ____ ____ of the United States.

4 Laura Bush is Mr. Bush's ____ ☆ ____ ____.

5 His daughters' names are Barbara and ____ ____ ○ ____.

His cat's name was △ ○ ⬓ ☆ ⬡ .

Mr. Lee's Store

At night, Mr. Lee locked the store and went home. That's when the fun began! The ketchup bottles stood in rows like bowling pins. Then the watermelon rolled down the aisle and knocked them down. The chicken wings flew around the room. Cans of soup stacked themselves higher and higher until they laughed so hard that they tumbled over. Carrots danced with bananas. Then it was morning. "Get back in your places!" called the milk jug. "Mr. Lee is coming!" Mr. Lee opened the door and went right to work.

> Story events that are make-believe and could never happen in real life are called **fantasy.**

Circle the cans that are fantasy.

Mr. Lee went home at night.	a talking milk jug	dancing bananas
laughing soup cans	Mr. Lee went to work.	chicken wings that can fly all by themselves
ketchup bottles and a watermelon bowling	dancing carrots	a grocery store

Cool Clouds

Have you ever looked up in the sky and seen a cloud that is shaped like an animal or a person? Big, white, puffy clouds float along like soft marshmallows. In cartoons, people can sit on clouds and bounce on them. But clouds are really just tiny drops of water floating in the air. You can understand what being in a cloud is like when it is foggy. Fog is a cloud near the ground!

Read each sentence below. If the sentence could really happen, color the cloud blue. If the sentence is fantasy, color it orange.

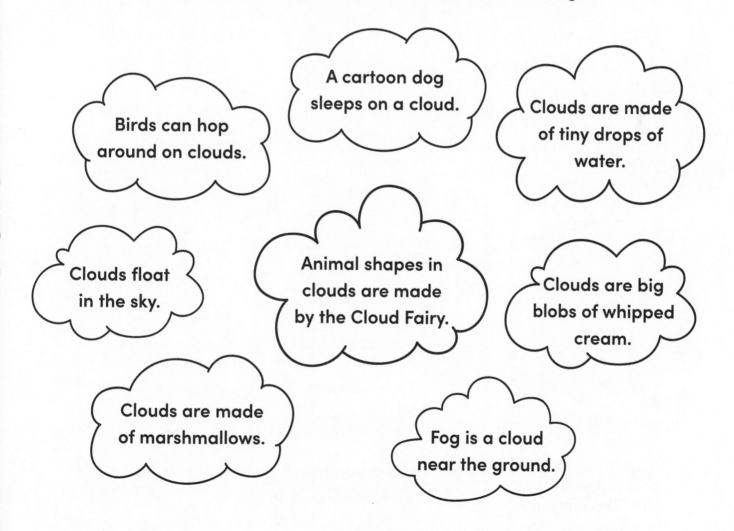

Birds can hop around on clouds.

A cartoon dog sleeps on a cloud.

Clouds are made of tiny drops of water.

Clouds float in the sky.

Animal shapes in clouds are made by the Cloud Fairy.

Clouds are big blobs of whipped cream.

Clouds are made of marshmallows.

Fog is a cloud near the ground.

Fun at the Farm

Read each sentence below. If it could be real, circle the picture.
If it is fantasy, put an X on the picture.

 Dairy cows give milk.

 Four little ducks swam in the pond.

 The pig said, "Let's go to the dance tonight!"

 The farmer planted pizza and sandwiches.

 The hay was stacked in the barn.

 The mouse ate the dinner table.

 The green tractor ran out of gas.

 The chicken laid golden eggs.

 The goat and the sheep got married by the big tree.

 Rain made the roads muddy.

 Horses sat on the couch and watched TV.

 The farmer baked a pumpkin pie.

 On another sheet of paper, write one make-believe sentence about the farmer's house and one real sentence about it.

Ready for School

Tara could hardly wait for school to start. Mom drove her to the store to buy school supplies. They bought pencils, crayons, scissors, and glue. When Tara got home, she wrote her name on all her supplies. She put them in a paper sack. The next day, Tara went to school, but the principal told her and the other children to go back home. A water leak had flooded the building. Oh, no! Tara would have to wait another whole week!

> To **sequence** means putting the events in a story in the order they happened.

Number the pictures in the order that they happened in the story.

Color the supplies that Tara bought.

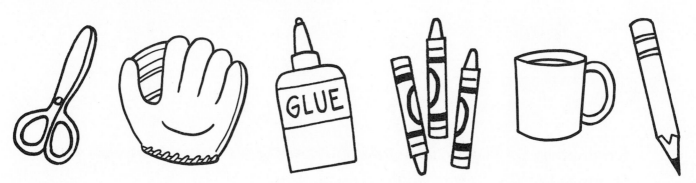

Swimming Lessons

Last summer, I learned how to swim. First, the teacher told me to hold my breath. Then I learned to put my head under water. I practiced kicking my feet. While I held on to a float, I paddled around the pool. Next, I floated to my teacher. Finally, I swam using both my arms and legs. I did it! Swimming is fun! This summer, I want to learn to dive off the diving board.

Number the pictures in the order that they happened in the story.

Unscramble the letters to tell what the person in the story wants to do next.

EALNR   OT   IVDE

___ ___ ___ ___ ___   ___ ___   ___ ___ ___ ___

☆ What would you like to learn to do? Draw four pictures on another sheet of paper to show how to do it.

Shapes in the Sky

Follow the directions.

1 Outline each star with a blue crayon. Then color each one red.

2 Color one moon yellow. Color the other one orange.

3 Draw a face on every sun.

4 Write the number of stars inside the star.

5 Write the number of moons inside the moon.

6 Write the number of suns inside the sun.

7 Add the three numbers you wrote together to find the total number of shapes.

_____ + _____ = _____

8 Which two shapes belong in the night sky?

_____ and _____

My Monster

Read the story.

I saw a scary monster that lived in a cave. It had shaggy fur and a long, striped tail. It had ugly, black teeth. Its three horns were shaped like arrows. Its nose was crooked. One of its feet was bigger than the other three. "Wake up! Time for breakfast," Mom said. Oh, good! It was only a dream.

Read the directions below carefully. Follow the directions. Look for key words such as *circle, underline,* and *draw*.

1 What did the monster's tail look like? Circle it.

2 What did the monster's horns look like? Circle them.

3 What did the monster's feet look like? Underline them.

4 Which of these is the correct picture of the monster? Draw a cave around it.

Fun at the Beach

Jack and Joni went to the beach today. Mom spread a blanket on the sand, and they had a picnic. It got very hot, so Jack and Joni jumped into the cold water. They climbed into a big yellow raft. The waves made the raft go up and down. Later, they played in the sand and built sandcastles. Jack and Joni picked up pretty shells. Joni found a sea star. What a fun day!

1 Color the pictures below that are from the story.
Put an X on the ones that don't belong.

2 In the third sentence, find two words that are opposites of each other and circle them with a red crayon.

3 What color was the raft? Show your answer by coloring the picture at the top of the page.

My New Rug

I bought a fancy rug today. It was made of brightly-colored yarn. I placed it on the floor in front of the TV and sat on it. All of a sudden, it lifted me up in the air! The rug and I flew around the house. Then out the door we went. High above the trees, we soared like eagles. Finally, it took me home, and we landed in my backyard.

How could that have happened? To find out, use your crayons to trace over each line. Use a different color on each line. Write the letter from that line in the box at the bottom of the rug.

T A I S W F I A L N Y A R G C T P E

Could this story really happen? Draw a rug around your answer.

Yes   No

Polly Want a Cracker?

Have you ever heard a parrot talk? Parrots are able to copy sounds that they hear. You can train a parrot to repeat words, songs, and whistles. But a parrot cannot say words that it has never heard. People can use words to make new sentences, but most parrots cannot.

Reach each sentence. If it is true, color the parrot under True. If it is false, color the parrot under False.

	True	False
1 You can teach a parrot to sing "Happy Birthday."		
2 You can ask a parrot any question, and it could give you an answer.		
3 A parrot can make up a fairy tale.		
4 If a parrot heard your mom say, "Brush your teeth," every night, he could learn to say it, too.		
5 It is possible for a parrot to repeat words in Spanish.		

You Be the Artist

An artist drew the pictures that are in this book. Now it is your turn to be the artist! Read each sentence very carefully. Draw exactly what you read about in the sentence.

Picturing a story can help the reader understand it better.

1 The green and yellow striped snake wiggled past the ants.

2 Wildflowers grew along the banks of the winding river.

3 On her sixth birthday, Shannon had a pink birthday cake shaped like a butterfly.

A Stormy Day

**Read the story below. Then go back and read each sentence again.
Add to the picture everything that the sentences describe.**

Big black clouds appeared in the sky. Lightning struck the tallest tree.
The scared cow cried, "Moo!" It rained hard. Soon there was a mud
puddle by the barn door. Hay blew out of the barn window.

Who Am I?

Circle the picture that answers the riddle.

1 I have feathers, I also have wings, but I don't fly.
I love to swim in icy water. Who am I?

2 I live in the ocean. I swim around looking for something
to eat. I have six more arms than you have. Who am I?

3 I like to watch movies and listen to music.
My grandchildren love my oatmeal cookies. Who am I?

4 I am an insect. If you touch me, I might bite you! I make tunnels
under the ground. I love to come to your picnic! Who am I?

What's Going On?

James was the first boy in Miss Lane's class to start feeling itchy. His scalp became so itchy that his mom came to take him home. The next day, Amy and Jana started feeling itchy too. The next Monday, six more children were absent. Finally, everyone got well and came back to school. But, this time Miss Lane was absent. Guess what was wrong with her!

Circle the correct answers.

1 What do you think was wrong with the children?

　　○ headache　　　○ head lice　　　○ broken arms

2 How do you know?

　　○ The children had itchy scalps.　　　○ The children came back to school.

3 How many children in all had this problem?

 2　　 5　　 9　　 4

4 Why do you think Miss Lane was absent? Write your answer.

_____

_____

Make a Cartoon

Read the sentences below each picture.
In the bubbles, write what each character could be saying.

Mr. Giraffe asked Mr. Zebra why he had stripes. Mr. Zebra didn't know.

Mr. Giraffe said that he should ask Mrs. Owl. Mr. Zebra agreed.

Mr. Zebra asked Mrs. Owl why he had stripes. Mrs. Owl laughed.

Mrs. Owl told Mr. Zebra that the Magic Fairy painted him that way!

Clean Your Room

Mom says, "Let's go out for ice cream! Clean your room, and then we will go." Your room is a mess. You need to put the blocks in the basket. The crayons must go in their box. The books must go on the shelf, and the marbles go in the jar. You can do it. Just think about that hot fudge sundae!

Grouping like things together makes it easier to remember what you need.

Draw a line from each item on the floor to where it belongs. Color what you could use in school red. Color toys blue.

Circle the food that does not belong in an ice cream store.

Going to the Mall

Read the words in the Word Bank. Write each word in the place where you would find these items at the mall.

Word Bank

tickets	sandals	tacos	beans	big screen
tulip bulb	peppers	fertilizer	popcorn	soil
sneakers	burritos	boots	shovel	candy

Sadie's Shoe Store

_____

_____

_____

_____

Pepe's Mexican Food

_____

_____

_____

_____

MOVIE TOWN CINEMA

_____

_____

_____

_____

GARDEN SHOP

_____

_____

_____

_____

My Favorites

This page is all about you! Read the categories and write your own answers.

My Favorite TV Shows

_____

_____

_____

My Favorite Foods

_____

_____

_____

My Favorite Sports

_____

_____

_____

Draw two of your favorite people here and write their names.

Favorite Color

_____

Favorite Holiday

_____

Favorite Song

_____

Favorite Movie

_____

Favorite School Subject

_____

Favorite Thing to Do With My Family

_____

Ouch!

Mia and Rosa were playing hospital. Mia was the patient, and Rosa was the doctor. Rosa pretended to take Mia's temperature. "You have a fever," she said. "You will have to lie down." Mia climbed onto the top bunk bed. "You need to sleep," Dr. Rosa said. Mia rolled over too far and fell off the top bunk. "O-o-o-h, my arm!" yelled Mia. Her mother came to look. It was broken!

What do you think happened next? Write your answer here.

_____

To find out if your answer is correct, finish the sentence below by coloring only the spaces that have a dot in them.

Mia had to go to

© Scholastic Inc.

What Will Sam Do?

One day, Sam was riding his bike to the baseball game. He had to be on time. He was the pitcher. Just ahead, Sam saw a little boy who had fallen off his bike. His knee was bleeding, and he was crying. Sam asked him if he was okay, but the boy couldn't speak. Sam knew the boy needed help getting home. If he stopped to help, he might be late for the game. Sam thought about it. He knew he had to do the right thing.

What do you think Sam will do next? There are two paths through the maze. Draw a line along the path that shows what you think Sam did next.

What sentence from the story gives you a hint about what Sam decided to do? Write the sentence below.

_____

_____

Riddle Fun

To solve the riddles in each box, answer the questions to find letter clues. Then write the letters in the blanks with the matching numbers.

> **What kind of food does a racehorse like to eat?**
>
> ___ ___ ___ ___   ___ ___ ___ ___
> 11   5   10   3   11   9   9   2

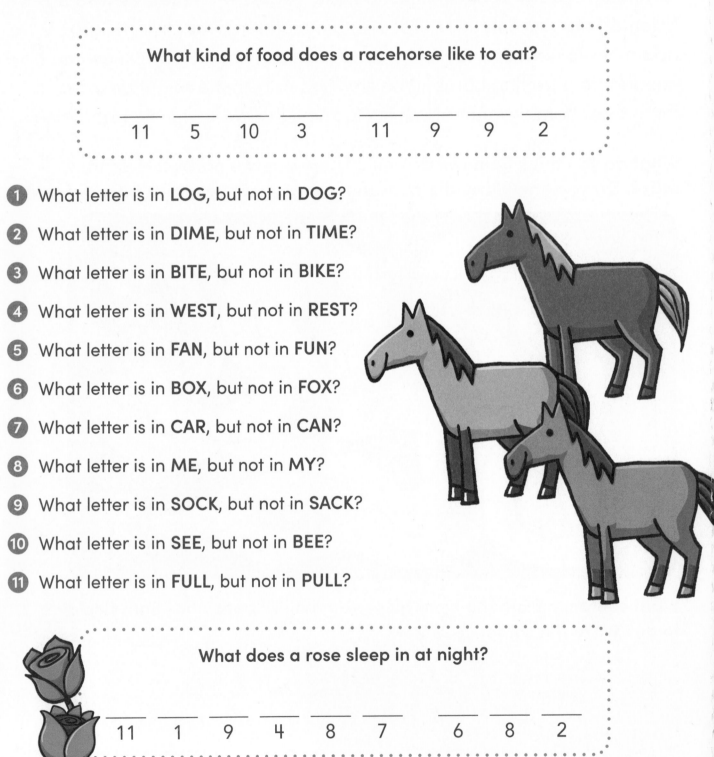

1. What letter is in **LOG**, but not in **DOG**?

2. What letter is in **DIME**, but not in **TIME**?

3. What letter is in **BITE**, but not in **BIKE**?

4. What letter is in **WEST**, but not in **REST**?

5. What letter is in **FAN**, but not in **FUN**?

6. What letter is in **BOX**, but not in **FOX**?

7. What letter is in **CAR**, but not in **CAN**?

8. What letter is in **ME**, but not in **MY**?

9. What letter is in **SOCK**, but not in **SACK**?

10. What letter is in **SEE**, but not in **BEE**?

11. What letter is in **FULL**, but not in **PULL**?

> **What does a rose sleep in at night?**
>
> ___ ___ ___ ___ ___ ___   ___ ___ ___
> 11   1   9   4   8   7   6   8   2

Twins

Holly and Polly are twins. They are in the first grade. They look alike, but they are very different. Holly likes to play softball and soccer. She likes to wear her hair braided when she goes out to play. She wears sporty clothes. Recess is her favorite part of school. Polly likes to read books and paint pictures. Every day she wears a ribbon in her hair to match her dress. Her favorite thing about school is going to the library. She wants to be a teacher some day.

Look at the pictures of Holly and Polly. They look alike, but there are differences. Can you find them? Circle the things that are different.

Underline the sentence that tells what is the same about Holly and Polly.

They play sports.   They love to paint.   They are in the first grade.

Soldier Moms

Juan's mother and Ann's mother are soldiers. Juan's mother is a captain in the Navy. She sails on the ocean in a large ship. Ann's mother is a pilot in the Air Force. She flies a jet. Juan and Ann miss their moms when they are gone for a long time. They write them letters and send them pictures. It is a happy day when their moms come home!

Draw a ☺ in the column under the correct mom. Some sentences may describe both moms.

	Juan's mom	Ann's mom	Both moms
She is a captain.			
She works on a ship.			
Sometimes she is gone for a long time.			
She is a pilot.			
Her child writes to her.			
She is in the Air Force.			
She is in the Navy.			
It is a happy time when she comes home.			
She flies a jet.			
She is a soldier.			

Dinosaur Clues

How do we know that dinosaurs were real? It is because their bones have been found in rocks. Sometimes scientists have found dinosaur footprints where mud later turned to stone. These kinds of rocks are called **fossils**. Fossils give us clues about how big the dinosaurs were. Some were small and some were very large. Scientists say a diplodocus was about as big as three school buses!

1 Color the picture that shows scientists working.

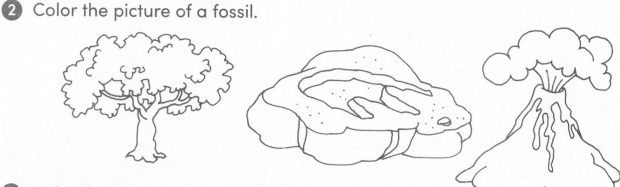

2 Color the picture of a fossil.

3 Color the picture of a diplodocus.

Amazing Animal Facts

Read each sentence. Then fill in the circle that tells the meaning of the underlined word.

1 Sea lions sometimes sleep in the water with one <u>flipper</u> up in the air.
○ an arm like a paddle
○ a beak
○ a feather

2 Even though whale sharks are the biggest fish in the world, they are <u>harmless</u> to people.
○ reddish brown
○ not dangerous
○ very tiny

3 Horses use their tails to <u>swat</u> pesky flies.
○ slap at
○ catch
○ eat

4 Snakes <u>shed</u> their old skins and grow new ones.
○ comb
○ burn
○ lose

5 Squirrels <u>bury</u> acorns and nuts to eat when winter comes.
○ bake
○ hide in the ground
○ search for

A Tiny Town

Have you ever seen a prairie dog town? That's where the prairie dogs live, but there are no buildings or houses. They live underground. They dig deep into the dirt making burrows. Along the burrows, here and there, are chambers for sleeping or storing food.

One chamber is lined with grass for the babies. Sometimes prairie dogs have unwanted guests in their town, like rattlesnakes!

Use the code below to learn what some of the words in the story mean. Copy the matching letters in the blanks.

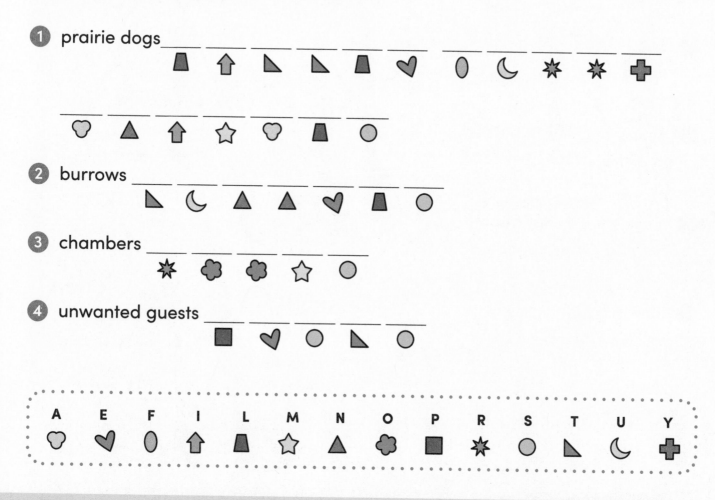

① prairie dogs

② burrows

③ chambers

④ unwanted guests

Oops!

Sandy went on a vacation in the mountains with her parents and little brother, Austin. They were staying in a small cabin without any electricity or running water. It was fun to have lanterns at night and to bathe in the cold mountain stream. The biggest problem for Sandy was she missed her best friend, Kendra. Sandy found her dad's cell phone and called Kendra. They talked for nearly an hour! When Sandy's dad went to call his office, the cell phone was dead. He was NOT a happy camper!

In a story, there is usually a reason something happens. This is the **cause**. What happens as a result is the **effect**.

Draw a line to match the first part of each sentence to the second part that makes it true.

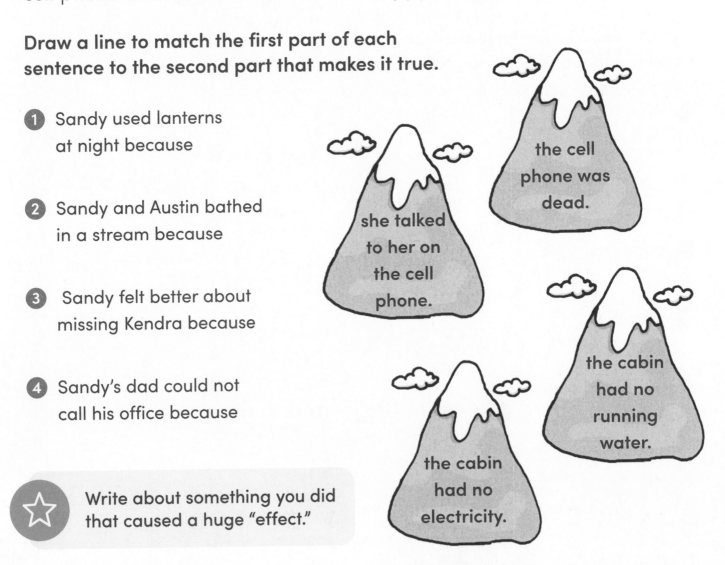

1 Sandy used lanterns at night because

2 Sandy and Austin bathed in a stream because

3 Sandy felt better about missing Kendra because

4 Sandy's dad could not call his office because

the cell phone was dead.

she talked to her on the cell phone.

the cabin had no running water.

the cabin had no electricity.

⭐ Write about something you did that caused a huge "effect."

Wanda Wiggleworm

Wanda Wiggleworm was tired of living alone in the flowerpot, so she decided to go out and meet other worms. Last night, Wanda went to the Bug Ball. She looked her best, all slick and slippery. Carl Caterpillar asked her to dance. They wiggled around and around to the music. All of a sudden they got tangled up. They tried to get free, but instead, they tied themselves in a knot! What did they do? They decided to get married and live happily ever after.

Unscramble each sentence about the text.
Write the new sentence on the lines below.

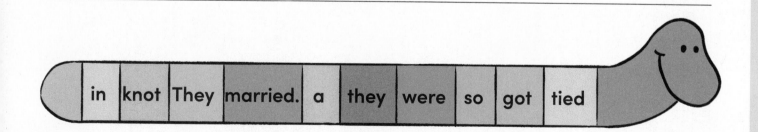

| tangled | when | got | danced. | they | Wanda and Carl | up |

_____

_____

| in | knot | They | married. | a | they | were | so | got | tied |

_____

_____

School Rules

It is important to follow the rules at school. Read each rule below.
Find the picture that shows what would happen if students DID NOT follow
that rule. Write the letter of the picture in the correct box.

1 You must walk, not run, in the halls. ☐

2 Do not chew gum at school. ☐

3 Come to school on time. ☐

4 When the fire alarm rings, follow the leader outside. ☐

5 Listen when the teacher is talking. ☐

6 Keep your desk clean. ☐

Mixed-Up Margie

Once upon a time there was a mixed-up queen named Margie. She got things mixed up. She wore her crown on her arm. She wore a shoe on her head. She painted her nose red! She used a fork to hold her hair in place. She wore a purple belt around her knees. The king didn't mind. He always wore his clothes backward!

> A **character** is a person or animal in a story. To help readers understand a character better, a story often gives details about the character.

Use the story and your crayons to help you follow these instructions:

1 Draw Margie a crown.

2 Draw her shoe.

3 Paint her nose.

4 Draw what goes in her hair.

5 Draw her belt.

Fill in the bubble next to the correct answer.

1 What makes you think Margie is mixed up?
○ the way she dresses
○ the way she talks

2 What makes you think the king is mixed up, too?
○ He talks backward.
○ He wears his clothes backward.

Miss Ticklefoot

I love Miss Ticklefoot. She is my first-grade teacher.

To find out more about her, read each sentence below. Write a word in each blank that tells how she feels. The Word Bank will help you.

Word Bank

| sad | scared | silly | worried | happy | surprised |

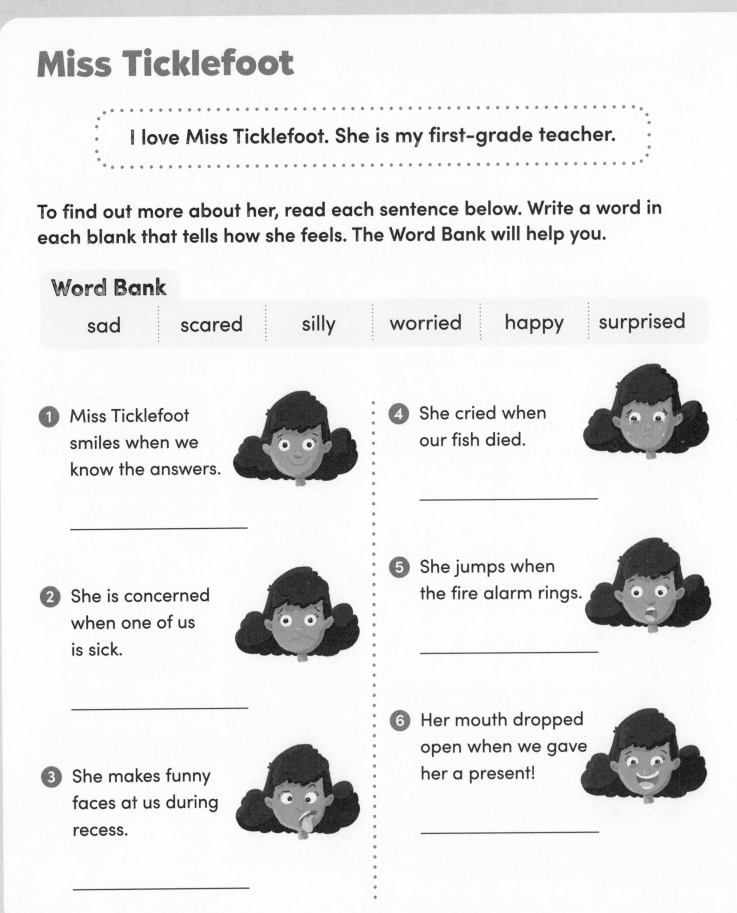

1 Miss Ticklefoot smiles when we know the answers.

_____

2 She is concerned when one of us is sick.

_____

3 She makes funny faces at us during recess.

_____

4 She cried when our fish died.

_____

5 She jumps when the fire alarm rings.

_____

6 Her mouth dropped open when we gave her a present!

_____

Different Friends

When Ty was four years old, he had two make-believe friends named Mr. Go-Go and Mr. Sasso. When there was no one else around, Ty talked to Mr. Go-Go while he played with his toys. Mr. Go-Go was a good friend. He helped put Ty's toys away. Mr. Sasso was not a good friend. Some days he forgot to make Ty's bed or brush Ty's teeth. Another day Dad said, "Oh, my! Who wrote on the wall?" Ty knew who did it... Mr. Sasso!

Read the phrase inside each crayon. If it describes Mr. Go-Go, color it green. If it describes Mr. Sasso, color it red. If it describes both, color it yellow.

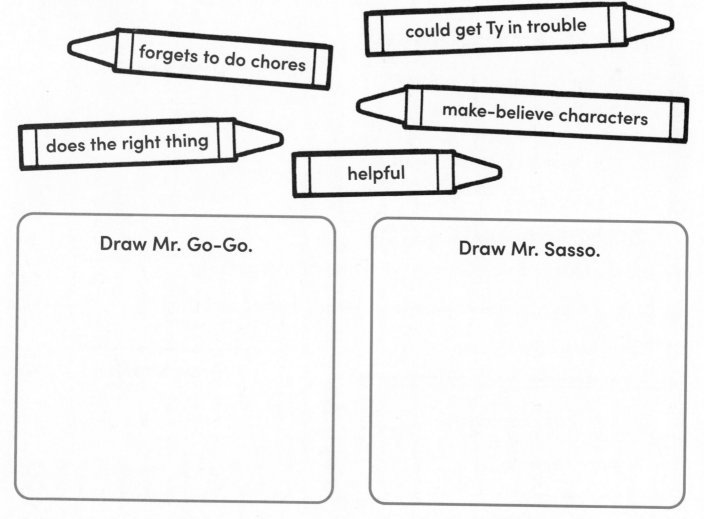

forgets to do chores

could get Ty in trouble

make-believe characters

does the right thing

helpful

Draw Mr. Go-Go.

Draw Mr. Sasso.

Poetry

A **poem** paints a picture with words. It often uses rhyming words.

Colorful Sky
When thunderstorms are near
Colored strips appear.
At the end, I'm told
There'll be a pot of gold.

Draw what it is.

1 Draw a red line under the word that rhymes with **near**.

2 Draw a green line under the word that rhymes with **told**.

What's That in the Sky?
It flies up in the sky.
It takes you way up high.
You see an airport, then
It takes you down again.

Draw what it is.

3 Draw a blue circle around the word that rhymes with **sky**.

4 Draw a brown circle around the word that rhymes with **then**.

5 Finish the two-line poem below:

I wish that I could see

A giant bumble _____.

Draw what it is.

A Fable

A fable is a story that teaches a lesson. This fable was written many, many years ago.

The Dog and His Shadow

A dog carried a piece of meat in his mouth. He crossed over a river on a low bridge. He looked down into the water and saw his reflection. It looked like another dog with a piece of meat larger than his. The dog snapped at the other dog's meat. When he did, his own meat dropped into the water. Now the dog didn't have any meat at all.

Draw a box around the lesson that the story teaches:

1 Two dogs are better than one.

2 Don't be greedy. Be happy with what you have.

Color only the pictures of things that you read about in the story:

Write a complete sentence telling what the dog should have done.

Library Books

A library has many different kinds of books. Have you ever read *The Rainbow Fish* by Marcus Pfister? It is a story about a very special fish. His scales were blue, green, and purple. He also had some shiny, silver scales. The other fish wanted him to share his shiny scales with them, but he said no. No one would be his friend. Later, he decided to give each fish one of his shiny scales. It was better to lose some of his beauty and have friends than to keep the scales to himself.

Connect the dots. You will see something from the book.

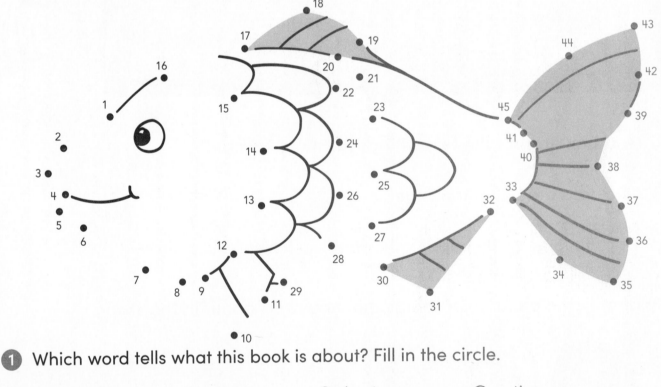

1 Which word tells what this book is about? Fill in the circle.

○ running   ○ lying   ○ sharing   ○ eating

2 Write the name of the author here.

_____

· SCHOLASTIC SUCCESS WITH ·

HANDWRITING

Aa

Trace and write.

A A A A A

a a a a a

A a

A Adam Ape is active.

Bb

Trace and write.

B B B

b b b

Bb

Betsy Bee buzzes.

Cc

Trace and write.

C C C C

c c c c

Cc

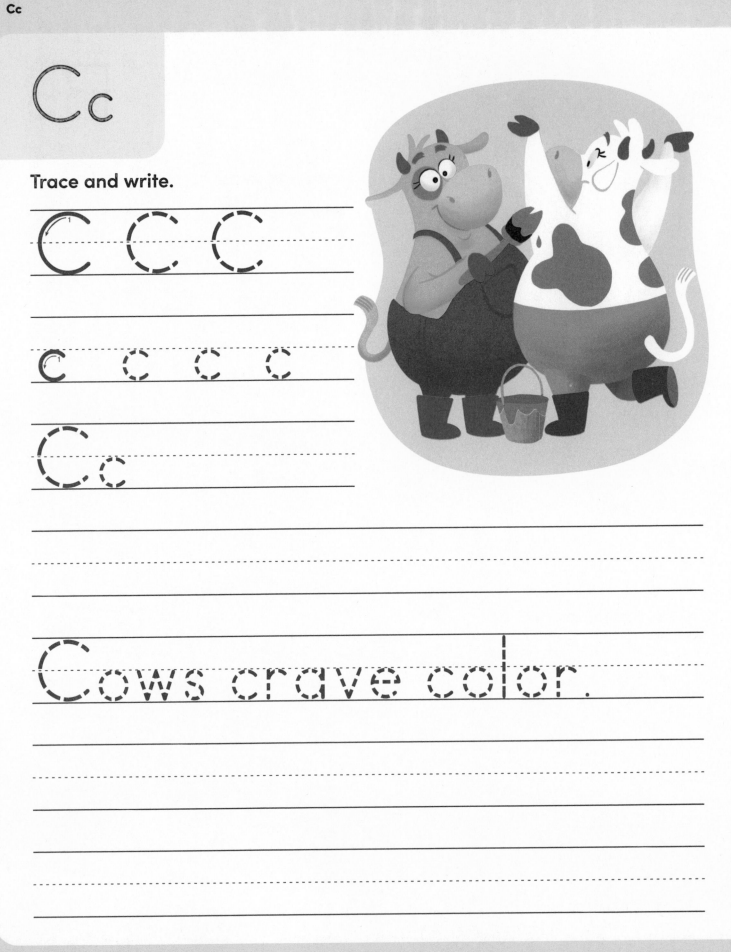

Cows crave color.

Dd

Trace and write.

D D D D

d d d d

Dd

Dandy Duck dances.

Ee

Trace and write.

E E E E

e e e e

Ee

Ellie Emu is elegant.

Ff

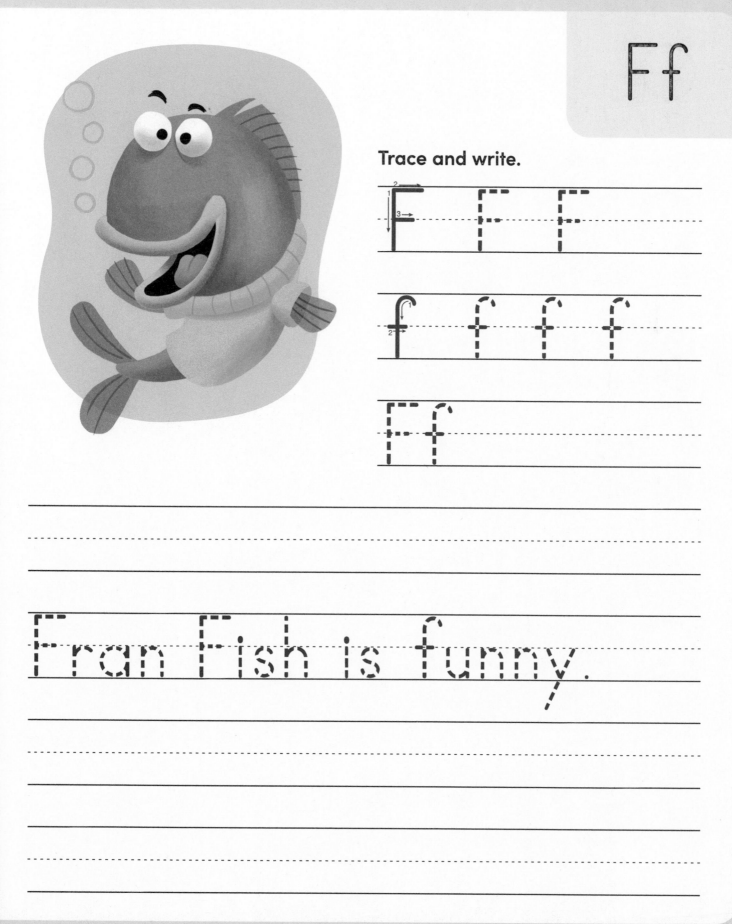

Trace and write.

F F F F

f f f f

F f

Fran Fish is funny.

Gg

Trace and write.

G G G

g g g

Gg

Gus Goose giggles.

Hh

Trace and write.

H H H H

h h h h

Hh

Hal Hippo is happy.

I i

Trace and write.

I I I

i i i i i

I i

Irina Iguana is itchy.

Jj

Trace and write.

J J J

j j j j

J j

Jim Jellyfish is jazzy.

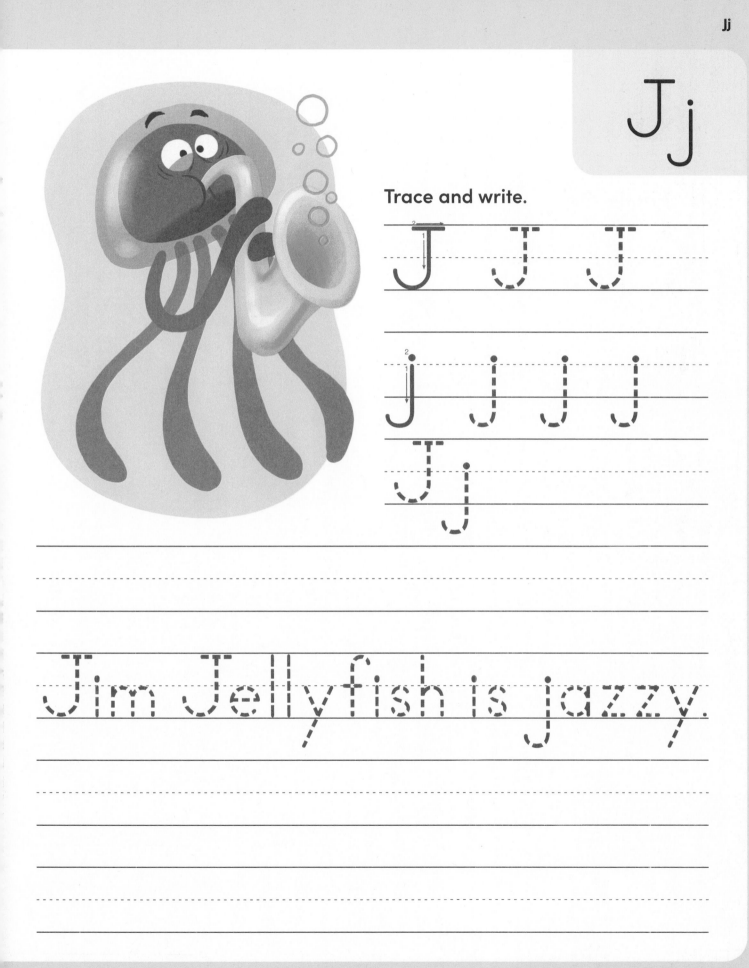

Kk

Trace and write.

K K K K

k k k k

K k

Kyle Kangaroo kicks.

Ll

Trace and write.

L L L L

l l l l

Ll

Lyle Lion looks lost.

Mm

Trace and write.

M M M M M

m m m m

Mm

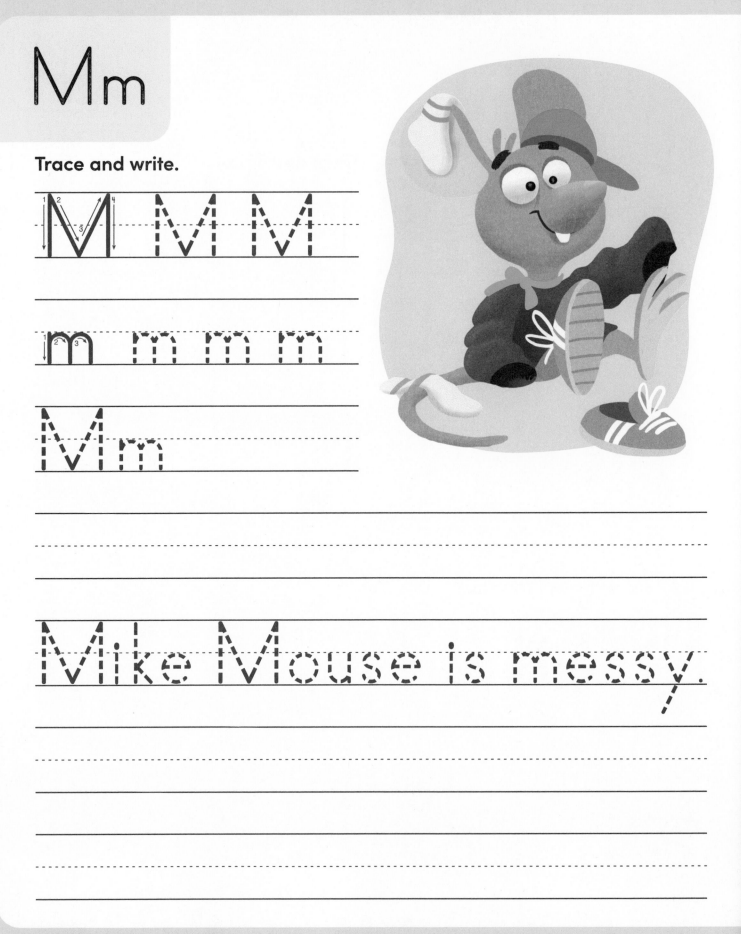

Mike Mouse is messy.

Nn

Trace and write.

N N N N

n n n n

Nn

Nikki Newt needs naps.

Oo

Oo

Trace and write.

Opal Owl sings opera.

Pp

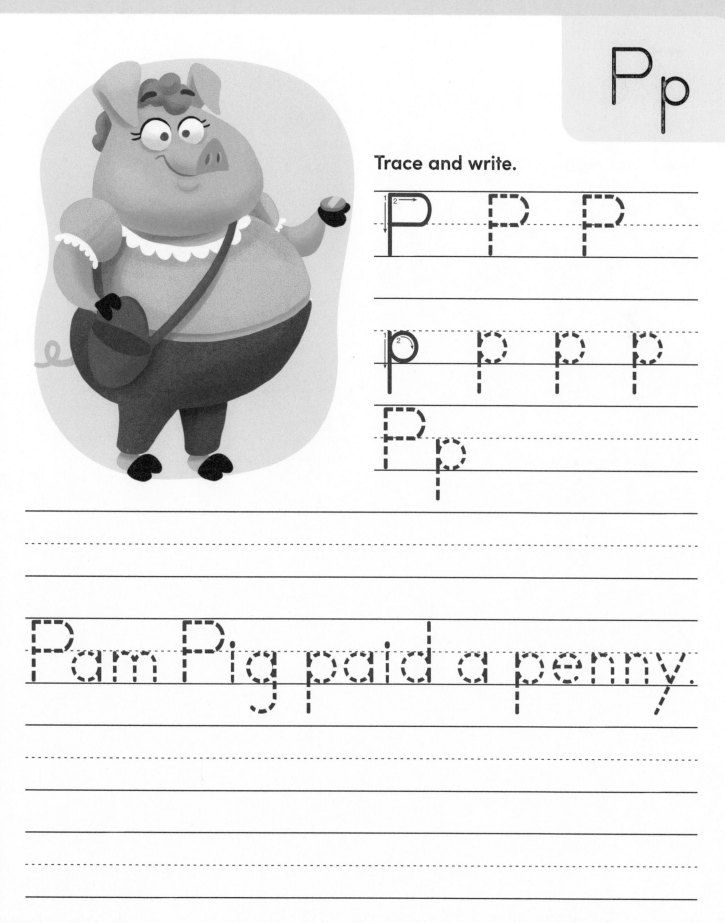

Trace and write.

P   P   P   P

p   p   p   p

Pp

Pam Pig paid a penny.

Qq

Trace and write.

Q Q Q

q q q q

Qq

Quinn Quail is quiet.

Rr

Trace and write.

R R R

r r r r

Rr

Rex Rabbit races.

Ss

Trace and write.

S S S

s s s s

Ss

Susanna Seal stars.

Tt

Trace and write.

T T T T

t t t t

T t

Tristan Toad is toothy.

Uu

Trace and write.

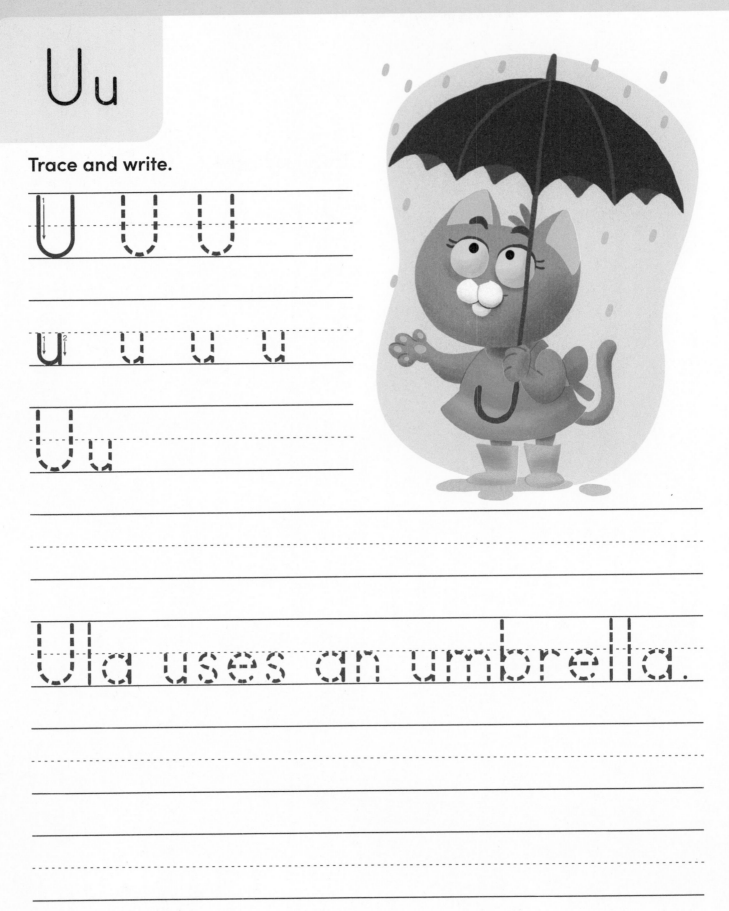

U U U

u u u u

Uu

Ula uses an umbrella.

V v

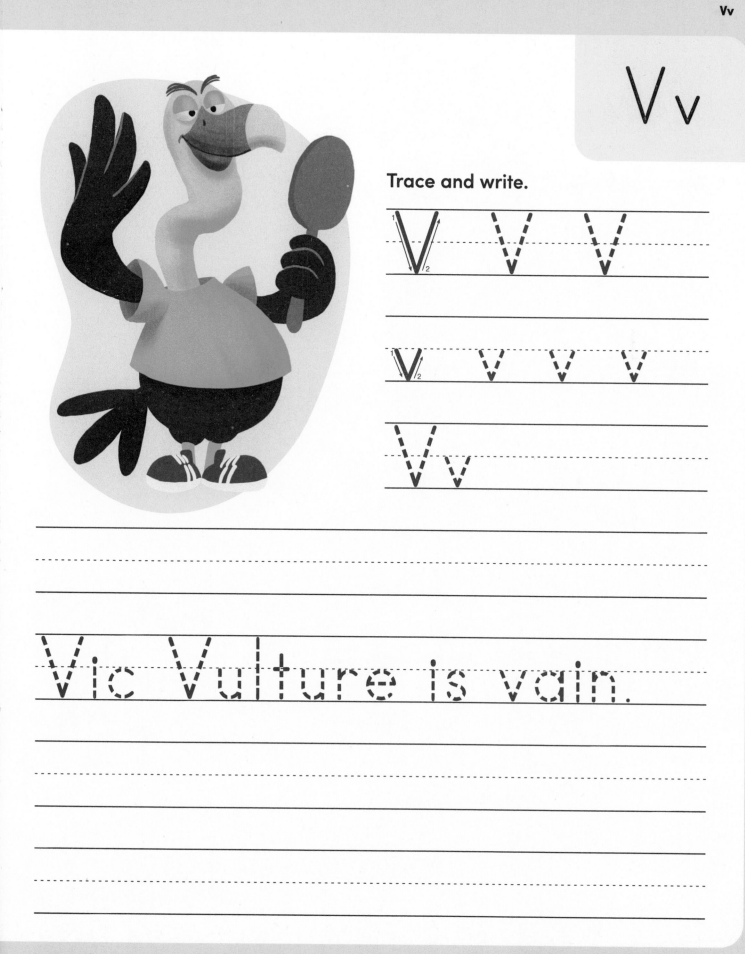

Trace and write.

V V V V

v v v v

V v

Vic Vulture is vain.

Ww

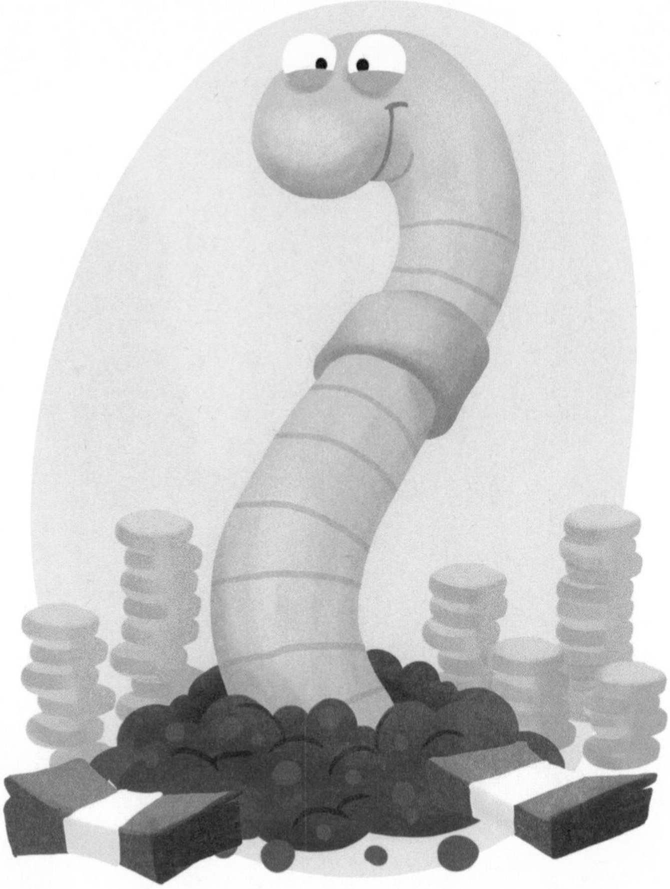

Trace and write.

W W W W

W W W W W

Ww

Will Worm is wealthy.

Xx

Trace and write.

X X X X

X X X X

X Xx

Xavier Fox is excited.

Yy

Trace and write.

Y Y Y Y

y y y y

Yy

Yvonne Yak yawns.

Zz

Trace and write.

Z Z Z Z

z z z z

Zz

Zoe Zebra is zany.

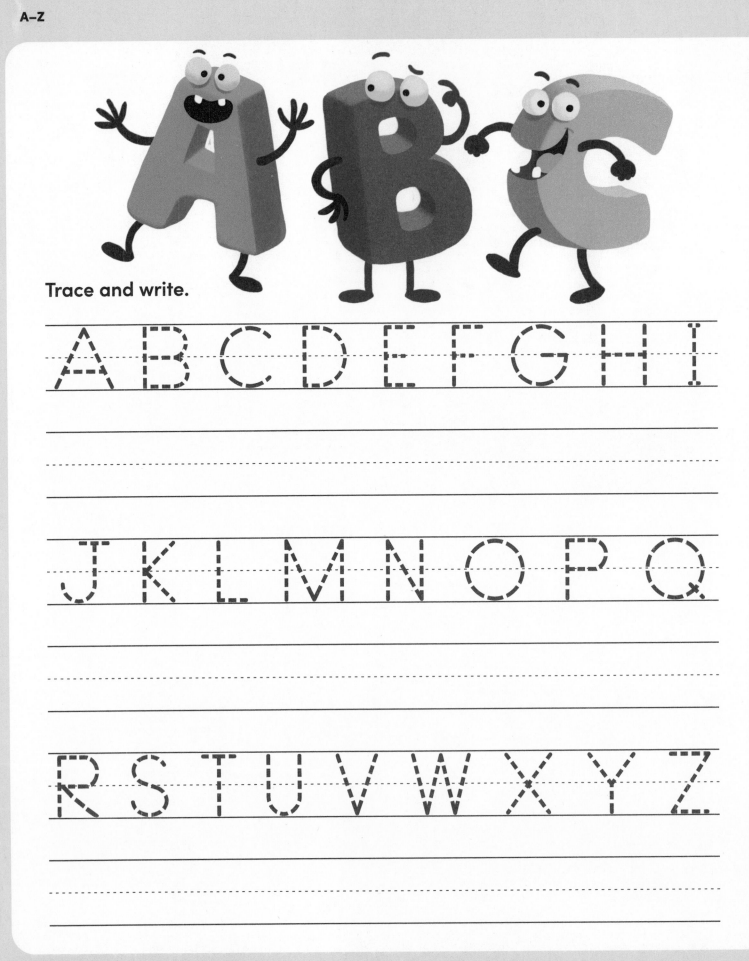

Trace and write.

A B C D E F G H I

J K L M N O P Q

R S T U V W X Y Z

Trace and write.

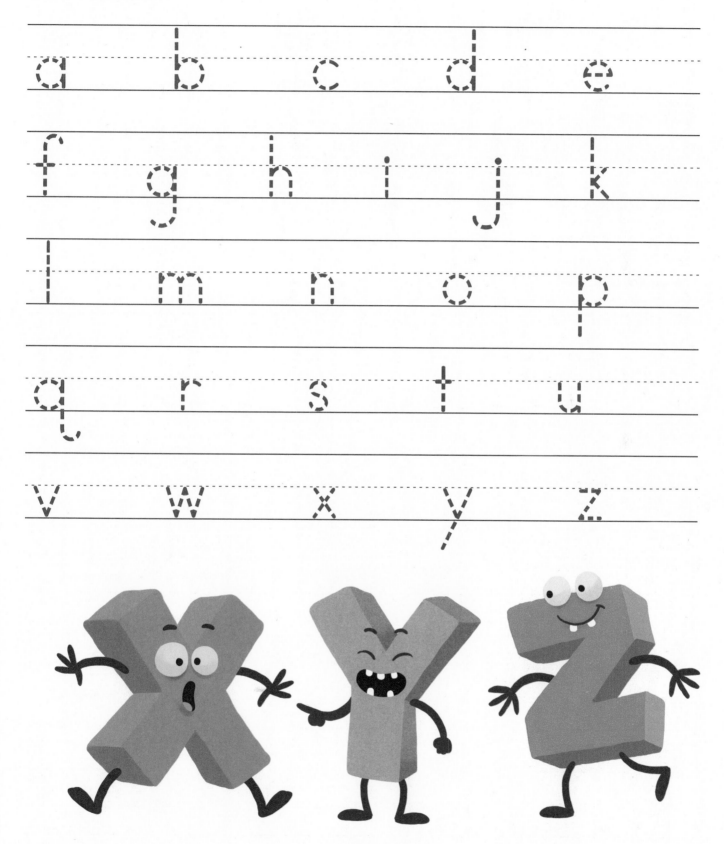

a   b   c   d   e

f   g   h   i   j   k

l   m   n   o   p

q   r   s   t   u

v   w   x   y   z

Trace and write.

Trace and write.

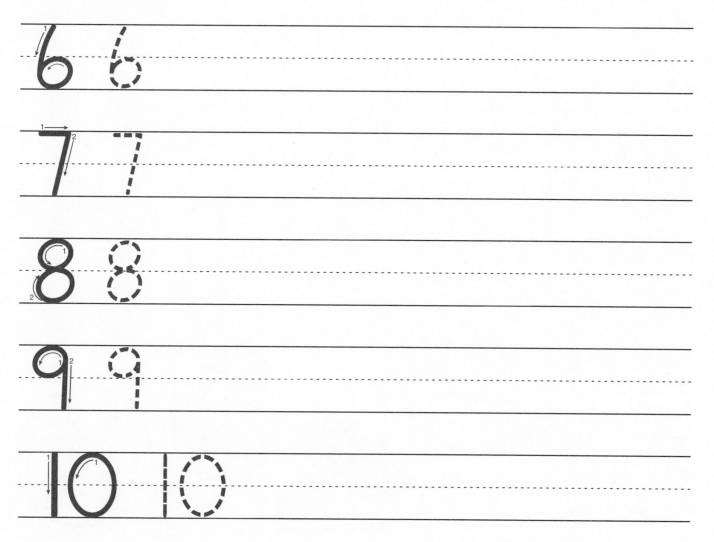

Color Words

Trace and write.

red

yellow

blue

green

orange

red

yellow

blue

green

orange

More Color Words

Trace and write.

purple

brown

black

white

pink

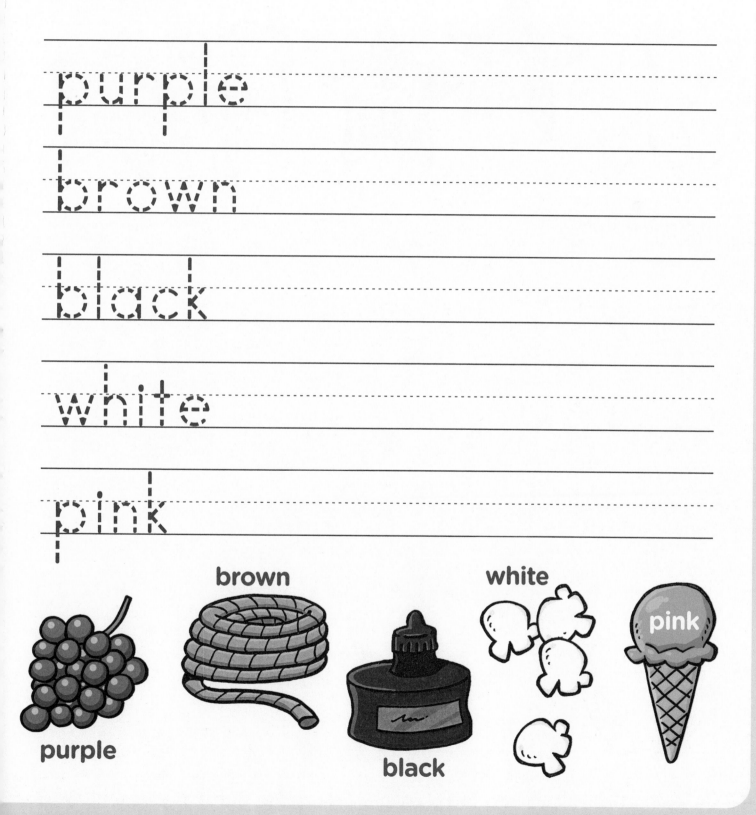

purple

brown

black

white

pink

Number Words

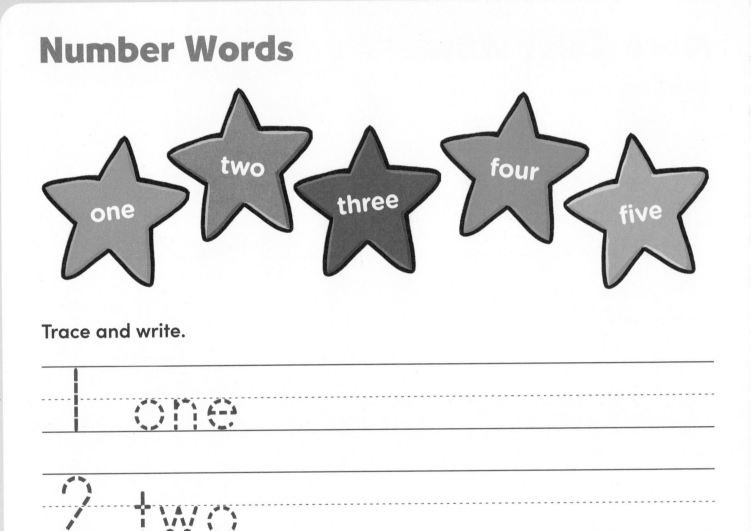

Trace and write.

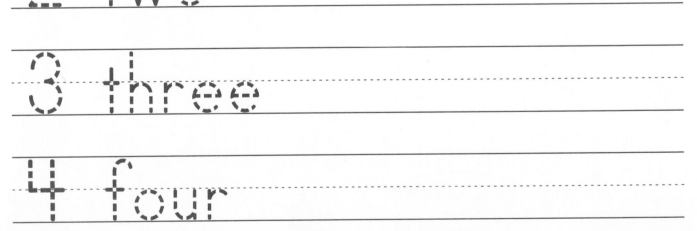

1 one

2 two

3 three

4 four

5 five

More Number Words

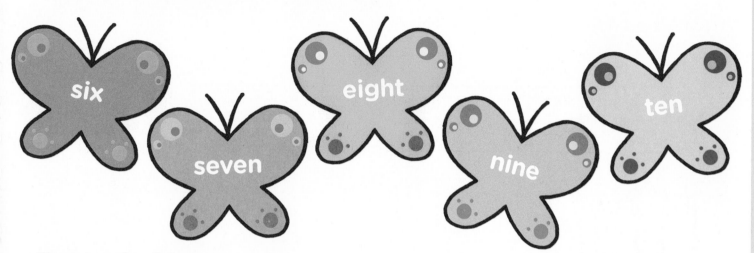

Trace and write.

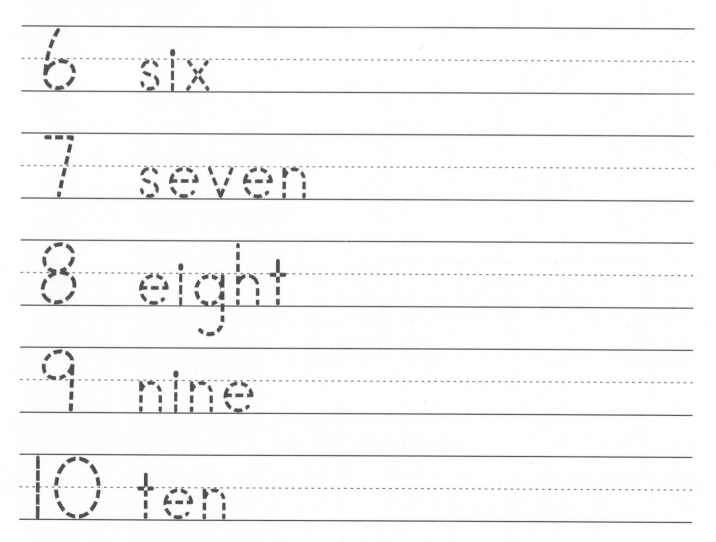

6 six

7 seven

8 eight

9 nine

10 ten

Shapes

Trace and write.

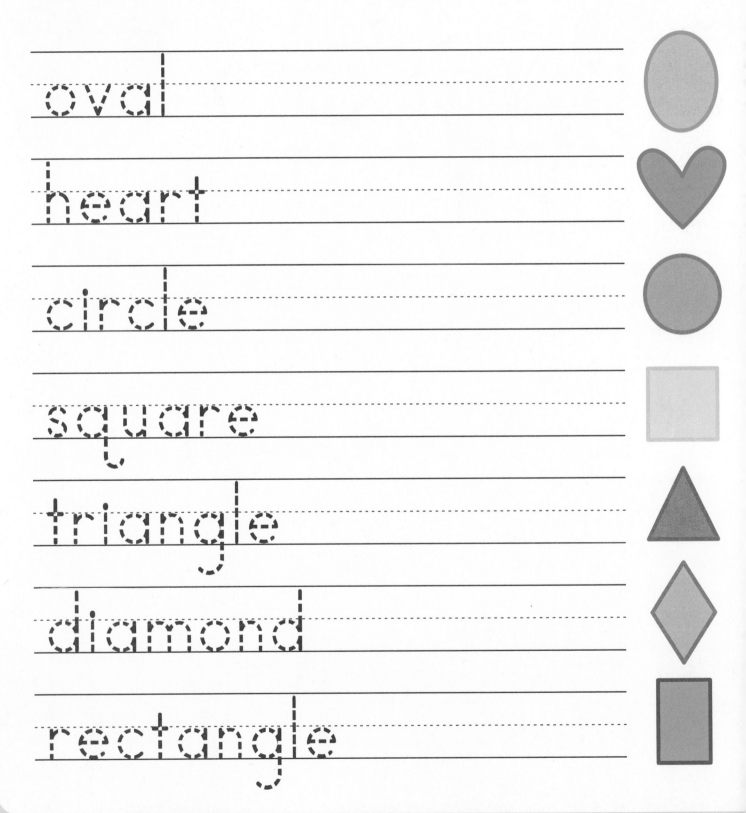

oval

heart

circle

square

triangle

diamond

rectangle

Days of the Week

Trace and write.

Sunday

Monday

Tuesday

Wednesday

Thursday

Friday

Saturday

Months

Trace and write.

January

February

March

April

May

June

Months

Trace and write.

July

August

September

October

November

December

Special Days

Write each special day.

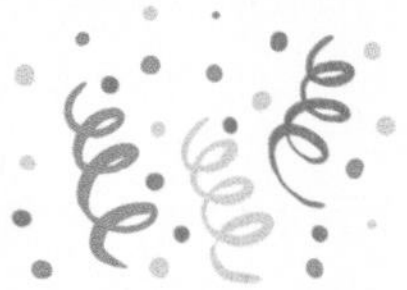

New Year's Day

_____
- - - - - - - - - - - - - - - - -
_____

Valentine's Day

_____
- - - - - - - - - - - - - - - - -
_____

Presidents' Day

_____
- - - - - - - - - - - - - - - - -
_____

St. Patrick's Day

_____
- - - - - - - - - - - - - - - - -
_____

Mother's Day

_____
- - - - - - - - - - - - - - - - -
_____

Father's Day

_____
- - - - - - - - - - - - - - - - -
_____

Fourth of July

_____

Special Days

Write each special day.

Labor Day

_____

- - - - - - - - - - - - - - - - - - -

Halloween

_____

- - - - - - - - - - - - - - - - - - -

Veterans' Day

_____

- - - - - - - - - - - - - - - - - - -

Thanksgiving

_____

- - - - - - - - - - - - - - - - - - -

Hanukkah

_____

- - - - - - - - - - - - - - - - - - -

Christmas

_____

- - - - - - - - - - - - - - - - - - -

Kwanzaa

_____

Animals From A to Z

Write the names of six animals on the lines below.

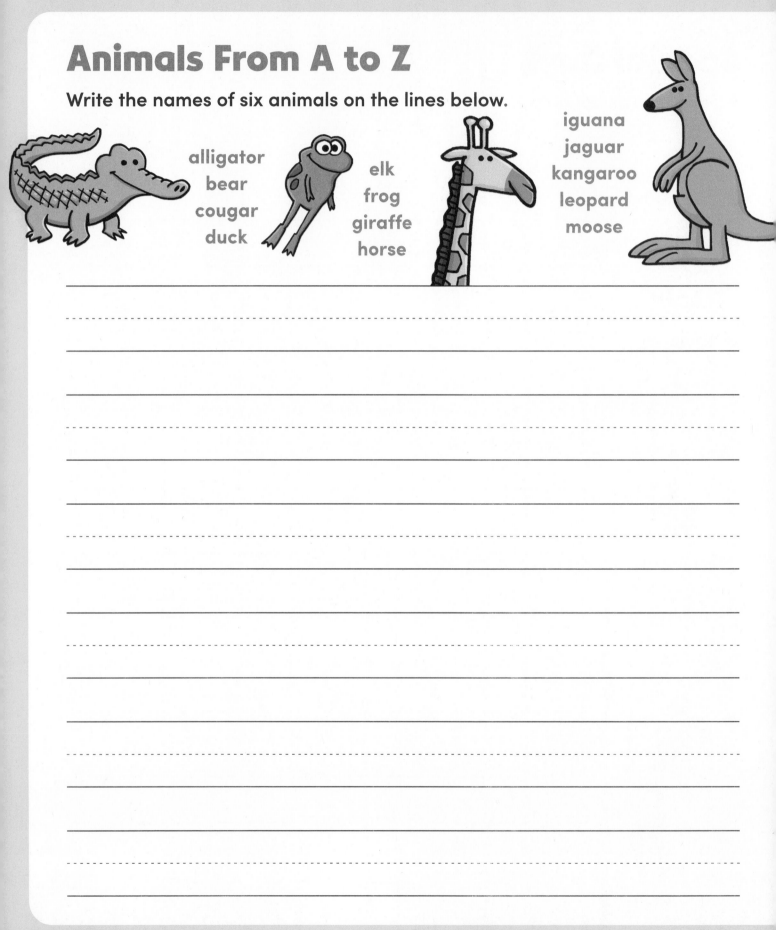

alligator
bear
cougar
duck

elk
frog
giraffe
horse

iguana
jaguar
kangaroo
leopard
moose

Animals From A to Z

Write the names of six animals on the lines below.

newt
ostrich
parrot
quail

raccoon
squirrel
tiger
urchin
vulture

whale
X-ray fish
yak
zebra

The Continents

Write the names of the continents.

Africa _____

_____

Antarctica _____

_____

Asia _____

_____

Australia _____

_____

Europe _____

_____

North America _____

_____

South America _____

_____

Africa

Antarctica

Australia

Asia

Europe

North America

South America

The Planets

Write the names of these planets.

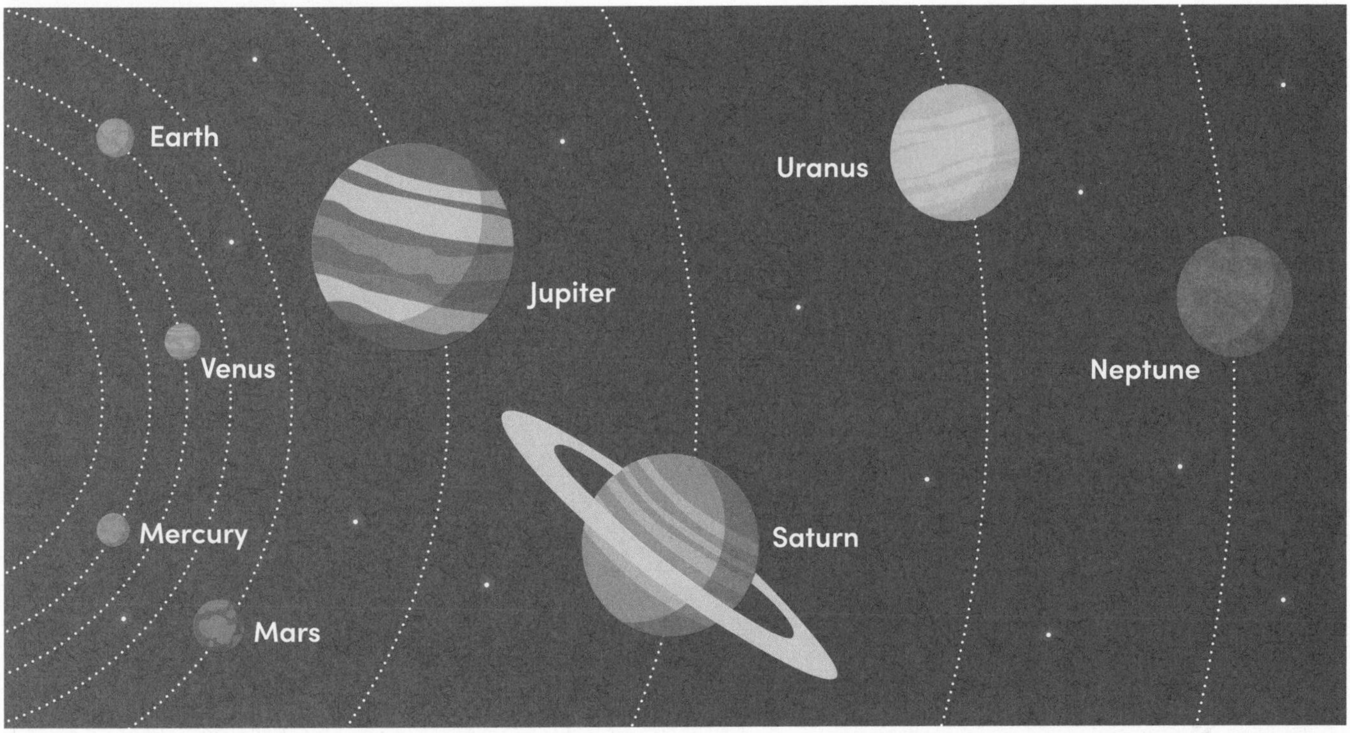

Earth

Uranus

Jupiter

Venus

Neptune

Mercury

Saturn

Mars

_____

has super handwriting!

KEEP UP THE GOOD WORK!

_____
signed

_____
dated

· SCHOLASTIC SUCCESS WITH ·

GRAMMAR

Capitalizing First Word

A sentence always begins with a capital letter.

Draw a line under the first letter in each sentence. Circle the two sentences that say something true about the picture.

1. The cat sat on a rat.

2. The hat is on the dog.

3. The rat sat on a hat.

4. The dog is on a mat.

5. The hat is on the cat.

6. The rat is on the cat.

Capitalizing First Word

Rewrite each sentence correctly on the line.

1 the cat sat.

_____

- -

_____

2 the dog sat.

_____

- -

_____

3 i see the cat.

_____

- -

_____

4 i can see.

_____

- -

_____

Capitalizing First Word

Read each sentence. Then fill in the circle next to the word with the capital letter that begins the sentence.

1 The cat is in the van.
- ○ cat
- ○ The

2 Jon can hop.
- ○ Jon
- ○ hop

3 Ants like jam.
- ○ jam
- ○ Ants

4 My dog can run.
- ○ My
- ○ dog

5 I like ham.
- ○ ham
- ○ I

6 We like the park.
- ○ We
- ○ like

Periods

Circle the period at the end of each sentence.

1 I see Jan.

2 We see Dan.

3 I go with Jan.

4 I go with Dan and Jan.

Draw a line under the last word in each sentence.
Add a period to each sentence.

1 We go to school

2 We like school

Periods

Write a period where it belongs in each sentence.
Read the sentences to a friend.

1 Dan is in the cab

2 The cat is in the cab

3 Mom is in the cab

4 We see Dan and Mom

· ·

Read the words. Write each word at the end of the correct sentence.

| van. | red. |

1 We can go in the _____

2 The van is _____

Periods

Read each group of words.
Fill in the circle next to the sentence that is written correctly.

1
- ○ The cat is on the mat.
- ○ the cat is on the mat
- ○ the cat on the mat

2
- ○ The rat sees the cat
- ○ The rat sees the cat.
- ○ the rat sees the cat

3
- ○ the cat and rat sit
- ○ The cat and rat sit
- ○ The cat and rat sit.

4
- ○ the rat is on the mat
- ○ the rat is on the mat.
- ○ The rat is on the mat.

5
- ○ The rat can hop.
- ○ The rat can hop
- ○ the rat can hop

Capitalizing *I*

Always write the word *I* with a capital letter.

Circle the word *I* in each sentence.

1 I like to hop.

2 I can hop to Mom.

3 Pam and I like to hop.

4 Mom and I can hop.

Draw what you like. Use the word *I* to write about it.

Capitalizing *I*

Read the sentences. Write *I* on the line.

1 _____ will ride.

2 _____ will swim.

3 Dad and _____ will sing.

4 Then _____ will read.

What will you do next? Write it on the line.

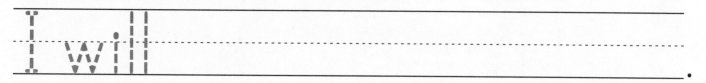

I will _____ .

Capitalizing I

Read each group of words.
Fill in the circle next to the sentence that is written correctly.

1 ○ i sit on a mat.
○ I sit on a mat.
○ i sit on a mat

2 ○ I see the van.
○ i see the van.
○ i see the van

3 ○ i like to nap.
○ I like to nap.
○ i like to nap

4 ○ Pam and I like cats.
○ Pam and i like cats.
○ pam and i like cats

5 ○ i like jam.
○ i like jam
○ I like jam.

6 ○ i like the park
○ I like the park.
○ I like the park

Simple Sentences

Circle who or what each sentence is about.

1 Pam ran.

2 Dan hops.

3 The cat sits.

4 The van can go.

Draw a line from each sentence to the picture of who or what the sentence is about.

1 Jon is hot.

2 The hat is on top.

3 The man sat.

Simple Sentences

Circle each sentence.

1 Bill

Bill paints.

3 plants flowers

Pat plants flowers.

2 likes to read

Tom likes to read.

4 cooks

Leon cooks.

Finish the sentence.

I like

Simple Sentences

Read each group of words. Fill in the circle next to the complete sentence.

1. ○ on a mat
   ○ The cat sits on a mat.
   ○ The cat

2. ○ I see Mom.
   ○ I see
   ○ Mom

3. ○ Ben
   ○ Ben can hop.
   ○ hop

4. ○ Pam and Dan like jam.
   ○ Pam and Dan
   ○ like jam

5. ○ my hat
   ○ I like
   ○ I like my hat.

6. ○ Dina rides a bike.
   ○ Dina bike.
   ○ rides a bike

Word Order

Words in a sentence must be in an order that makes sense.

Read each group of words. Draw a line under the word that should go first in each sentence.

1. dots. I like
2. like We hats.
3. Pam dots. likes
4. hats with dots. We like

Now write each group of words in the correct order.

1.

2.

3.

4.

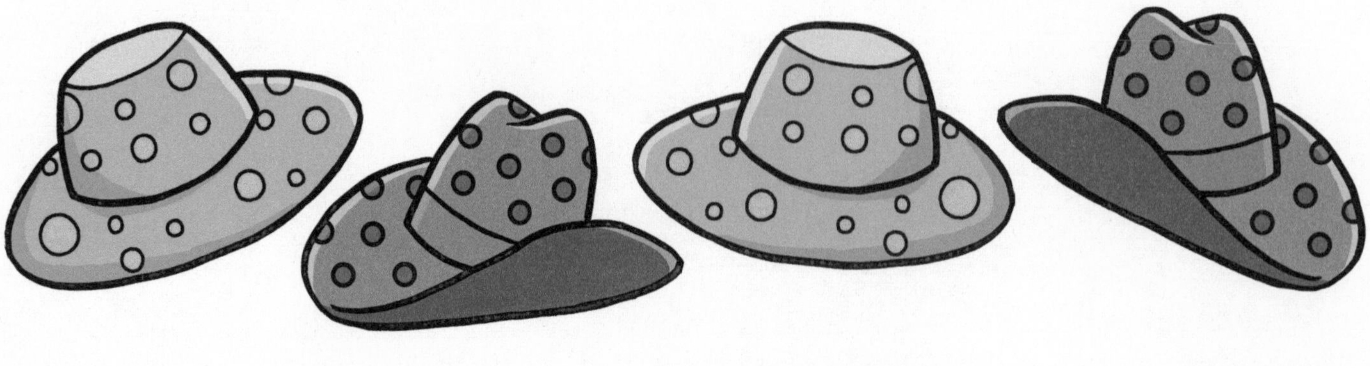

Word Order

Read each group of words. Write them in the correct order on the lines.

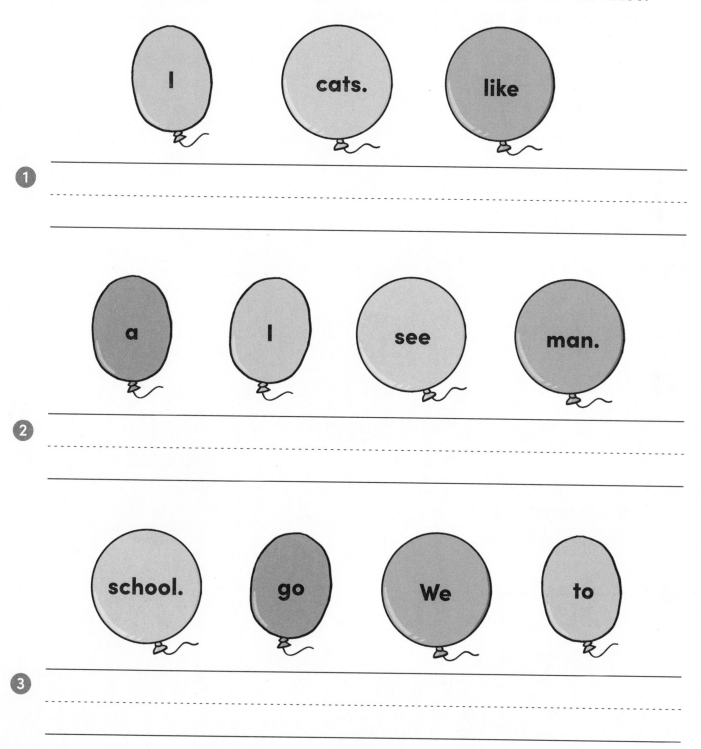

1 _____

2 _____

3 _____

Word Order

Read each group of words. Fill in the circle next to the words that are in an order that makes sense.

1 ○ I red dots. see
○ I see red dots.
○ dots red

2 ○ fat. cat The is
○ is fat. The cat
○ The cat is fat.

3 ○ likes Ben jam.
○ Ben likes jam.
○ jam. likes Ben

4 ○ Dan is in a big van.
○ big Dan a van. is in
○ van big Dan in a is

5 ○ We like the hat.
○ the like hat. We
○ We hat. the like

6 ○ Jada rides a bike.
○ bike rides. Jada a
○ bike. a Jada rides

Question Sentences

Read each sentence. Circle each question mark.

1. Who hid the hat?

2. Is it on the cat?

3. Can you see the hat?

4. Is it on the man?

- -

Write two questions. Draw a line under each capital letter at the beginning of each question. Circle the question marks.

1. _____

2. _____

Question Sentences

Draw a line under each sentence that asks a question.
Circle the question mark.

1. Who hid the cat?

2. Can the cat see the rat?

3. The cat is in the van.

4. Can the van go?

· ·

Read the sentences. Circle each sentence that asks something.

1. Can we sit in the van?

   We can sit in the van.

2. Dan can nap in the van.

   Can Dan nap in the van?

Question Sentences

Read the sentences. Fill in the circle next to the sentence that asks a question.

1 ○ Who hid my hat?
○ My hat is with him.
○ My hat is big.

2 ○ The hat has spots.
○ The hat has dots.
○ Did the hat have dots?

3 ○ Can you see the hat?
○ You can see the hat.
○ She can see the hat.

4 ○ Jan likes my hat.
○ Did Jan like my hat?
○ Jan did like my hat.

5 ○ Dan can get a hat.
○ Dan likes hats.
○ Did Dan get a hat?

Naming Words

Read each sentence. Draw a line under the word or words that name the person, place, animal, or thing in each sentence.

> A naming word names a person, place, animal, or thing.

1 The pig is big.

2 The pan is hot.

3 Pam hid.

4 Can you run up the hill?

Draw a line from each sentence to the picture that shows the naming word in that sentence.

1 The sun is hot.

2 Sam ran and ran.

3 Is the cat fat?

Naming Words

Circle the naming words in the sentences.

1 Al can go in a van.

3 Pat ran up the hill.

2 The cat sat on a mat.

4 Dan and Jan will mop.

Draw a picture of a person, place, animal, or thing.
Write a sentence about your picture. Circle the naming word.

Naming Words

Read each sentence. Fill in the circle next to the naming word.

1 I see a big cat.

○ see ○ big ○ cat

2 The rat ran fast.

○ ran ○ rat ○ fast

3 Can you see the map?

○ Can ○ map ○ see

4 The van is tan.

○ van ○ is ○ tan

5 The fan is not on!

○ not ○ on ○ fan

Capitalizing Special Names

Draw a line under the special name in each sentence.
Then circle the first letter or letters in that name.

> The names of specific people, places, and pets are special. They begin with capital letters.

1. They go to Hill Park.

2. Don sees the cat.

3. Pam sees the ham.

4. They like Frog Lake.

Write the special name of a person, place, or pet you know.

Capitalizing Special Names

Circle each special name.
Draw a line under each capital letter in each name.

1 I am Pam.

2 Ron likes the lake.

3 I sit on Ant Hill.

4 He likes Bat Lake.

Read the special names in the box.
Write the special name for each picture.

| Spot | Hill Street |

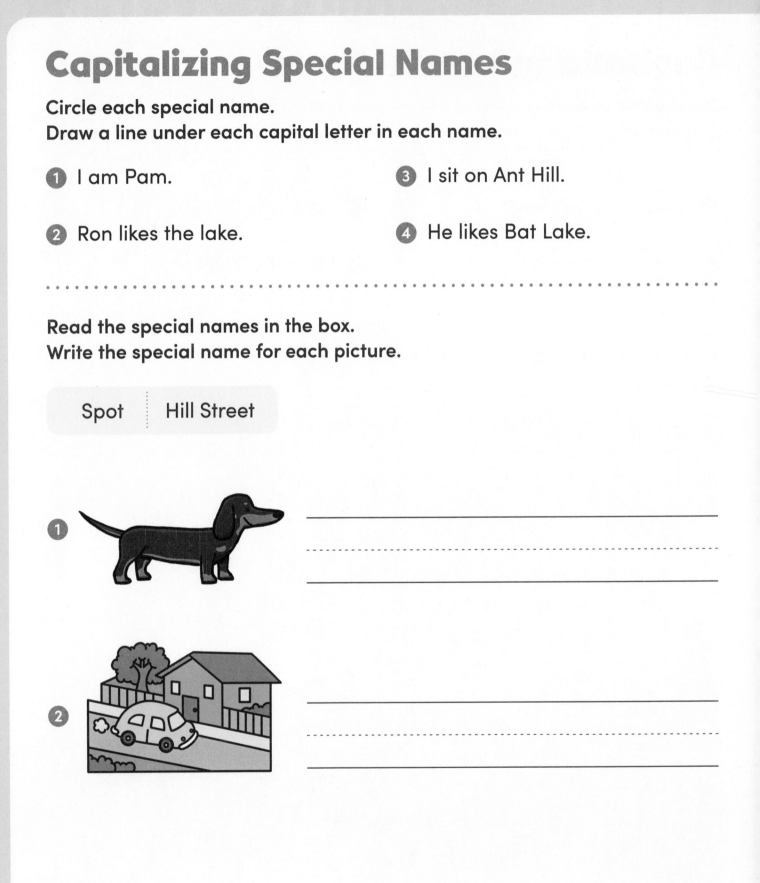

1

2

Capitalizing Special Names

Read each sentence. Fill in the circle next to the special name.

1. Can Don go to the picnic?
   ○ picnic
   ○ Don
   ○ Can

2. The picnic will be on Pig Hill.
   ○ Pig Hill
   ○ picnic
   ○ The

3. Jan will go to the picnic.
   ○ go
   ○ picnic
   ○ Jan

4. The hill is on Jam Street.
   ○ hill
   ○ The
   ○ Jam Street

5. She will go to Ham Lake.
   ○ She
   ○ Ham Lake
   ○ will

Action Words

An action word tells what happens.

Read each sentence.
Circle the word that tells what happens.

1 The hen clucks.

2 The cat ran.

3 Pam hid.

4 The dog naps.

Read the words. Use the words to finish the sentences.

run	see

_____
- - - - - - - - - - - - - - - - -

1 I will _____ up the hill.

_____
- - - - - - - - - - - - - - - - -

2 I _____ a big pig.

Action Words

Look at each picture. Read the words. Write the action word.

1   I can see.

2   The cat sits.

3   Dad mops.

4   We run fast.

5   It hops a lot.

Action Words

Read each sentence.
Fill in the circle next to the action word.

1 I sit on a hill.

○ I   ○ sit   ○ hill

2 The rat ran fast.

○ ran   ○ rat   ○ fast

3 We mop a lot.

○ We   ○ lot   ○ mop

4 The dog digs up sand.

○ dog   ○ sand   ○ digs

5 Pam hops up and down.

○ hops   ○ up   ○ Pam

Describing Words

Read each sentence. Circle the word that tells about the cat.

A describing word tells more about a person, place, animal, or thing.

1. I see a big cat.

2. The fast cat ran.

3. My cat is bad.

4. The fat cat naps.

....

Look at each cat. Circle the word that tells about it.

1.

big   little

2.

big   little

Describing Words

Look at each picture. Circle the words that tell about it.

1

big   fast

little   blue

2

happy   hot

big   cold

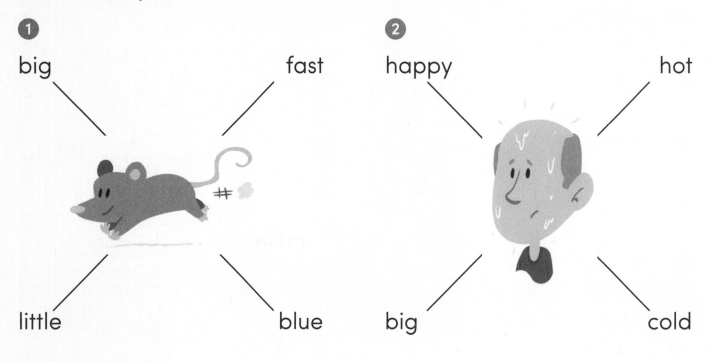

. . . .

Draw a line between each sentence and the picture that shows what it describes.

1 It is fat.

2 They are little.

Describing Words

Read each sentence. Fill in the circle next to the describing word.

1 The silly cat can play.
- ○ silly
- ○ cat
- ○ play

2 The black dog naps.
- ○ dog
- ○ black
- ○ naps

3 A green frog can hop.
- ○ frog
- ○ green
- ○ hop

4 The fast rat ran.
- ○ fast
- ○ ran
- ○ rat

5 The cow is big.
- ○ cow
- ○ is
- ○ big

6 The gray cat sleeps.
- ○ cat
- ○ sleeps
- ○ gray

Telling Sentences

A telling sentence tells something.

Circle the capital letter at the beginning of each telling sentence. Then circle the period at the end of each telling sentence.

1. I see the basket.

2. The cat is in the basket.

3. Hats can go in it.

4. The sock can go in it.

Draw a line under each telling sentence.

1. I can fill the basket.

2. Can you get the mop?

3. We can clean.

4. Do you like the vase?

5. He jogs on Mondays.

6. She helps her father cook.

Telling Sentences

Draw a line to match each sentence with the picture that shows what the sentence tells.

1 She has a mop.

2 The dog is on top.

3 Dan gets the hats.

4 Ron can clean spots.

· ·

Read the sentences.
Circle the capital letter and period in the telling sentence.

1 Put it in the pot.   **2** Is it in the pan?

Telling Sentences

Read the sentences. Fill in the circle next to each sentence that tells something.

1 ○ Can you get the basket?
○ You can get it.
○ Can you fill it?

2 ○ What can go in it?
○ Will the hat go in?
○ The hat is in the basket.

3 ○ Can we fill it?
○ We can fill the basket.
○ Will you fill it?

4 ○ The basket is big.
○ Is the basket big?
○ Why is it big?

5 ○ A cat cannot go in it.
○ Can a cat go in?
○ Will a cat go in it?

6 ○ Can the toys go in
   the basket?
○ I put the toys in the basket.
○ What is in the basket?

Exclamation Sentences

Read each sentence. Circle each exclamation mark. Draw a line under the capital letter at the beginning of each sentence.

Exclamatory sentences show strong feelings, such as excitement, surprise, or fear. They end with exclamation marks. (!)

1 Help! The cat is on top!

2 Get the cat!

3 This cat is bad!

4 Uh-oh! The cat is wet!

Read each set of sentences. Draw a line under the sentence or sentences that show strong feeling.

1 Oh, my! Get the dog!

Let's get the dog.

2 The dog runs.

Oh! The dog runs!

Exclamation Sentences

Choose the sentence in each pair that shows strong feeling.
Write it on the line. Put an exclamation mark at the end.

1 Run to the show   We will go to the show

- -

2 I'm late for it   Oh my, I'm very late

- -

3 What a great show   I liked the show

- -

4 The floor is wet   Watch out, the floor is wet

- -

5 We had fun   Wow, we had lots of fun

- -

Exclamation Sentences

Read each group of sentences. Fill in the circle next to the sentence or sentences that show strong feeling.

1. ○ The cow is on the hill.
○ The cow likes grass.
○ Yes! The cow can kick!

2. ○ The rat will run.
○ That rat runs fast!
○ The rat can hop.

3. ○ The pot can get hot.
○ The pot is hot!
○ Fill the pot with mud.

4. ○ That cat is bad!
○ That cat naps.
○ Is the cat on the mat?

5. ○ Oh, no! A frog is in my house!
○ A frog hops.
○ The frog is green.

Punctuation Power

Each sentence is missing a punctuation mark.
Draw a line to match each punctuation mark to a sentence.

1 Let's go

2 I am a kid

3 Why doesn't the clock work

4 Do you have a hat

5 This game is fun

6 I play soccer

7 What's your name

8 The beach is great

9 My name is Paul

!
?
!
?
!
?

Singular/Plural Nouns

Read each sentence. Draw a line under each naming word that means more than one.

1 I see hats and a cap.

2 The girls swim.

3 It sits on eggs.

4 Pam can pet cats.

Read each sentence. Write the naming word that means more than one.

1 The mugs are hot.

2 Mud is on my hands.

Singular/Plural Nouns

Read the sets of sentences. Draw a line under the sentence that has a naming word that names more than one.

1 Jan has her mittens.

Jan has her mitten.

2 Jan runs with her dogs.

Jan runs with her dog.

3 She will run up a hill.

She will run up hills.

4 The dogs can jump.

The dog can jump.

. . . .

Look at each picture. Read each word.
Write the plural naming word that matches the picture.

1 cat _____

2 sock _____

Singular/Plural Nouns

Read each sentence. Fill in the circle next to the naming word that means more than one.

1 Jim gets mud on his hands.
- ○ gets
- ○ hands
- ○ mud

2 The dogs dig fast.
- ○ dig
- ○ fast
- ○ dogs

3 The frogs hop.
- ○ The
- ○ frogs
- ○ hop

4 Pam can fill the pots with mud.
- ○ pots
- ○ mud
- ○ fill

5 The ants are on the plant.
- ○ ants
- ○ plant
- ○ are

6 The kittens are on the sofa.
- ○ sofa
- ○ on
- ○ kittens

Action Words

Read each sentence.
Circle the word that tells what happens.

1 The hen sits.

2 The dog digs.

3 Mom sees the hen.

4 The cat naps.

....

Read the words. Use the words to finish the sentences.

sees	run

_____

1 She _____ eggs.

_____

2 It can _____ fast.

Action Words

Look at the pictures. Read the action words in the box.
Write the correct action word on the line.

| talk | play | dance | run |

_____

1 Sue and Al _____ball.

_____

2 The bears _____.

_____

3 Rabbit and Pig _____.

_____

4 Tami and Lee _____ fast.

Action Words

Read each sentence. Fill in the circle next to the action word.

1 The hen sits.
- ○ hen
- ○ sits
- ○ The

2 The green frog hops
- ○ frog
- ○ green
- ○ hops

3 The big pig ran.
- ○ big
- ○ pig
- ○ ran

4 The cat naps in the van.
- ○ naps
- ○ cat
- ○ van

5 The dog digs.
- ○ digs
- ○ dog
- ○ The

6 The cute kitten jumps.
- ○ jumps
- ○ cute
- ○ The

Naming Words

Read each sentence. Draw a line under the naming word.

> A naming word names a person, place, animal, or thing.

1 We play at school.

2 The girl kicks.

3 The ball is fast.

4 The friends run.

. . . .

Look at each box. Circle the naming word that belongs in that box.

Person	Place	Animal	Thing
girl	ball	cup	Pam
school	Bill	Jonah	man
ball	school	rabbit	ball

Naming Words

Read each sentence. Circle each naming word.
Draw a line to match the sentence to the picture of the naming word.

1 Run and kick in the park.

2 Kick with a foot.

3 Kick the ball.

4 The girl will run.

5 Kick into the net.

Naming Words

Read each sentence. Fill in the circle next to the word that names a person, place, animal, or thing.

1 Play in the park.
- ○ play
- ○ Let's
- ○ park

2 Kick the ball.
- ○ ball
- ○ the
- ○ kick

3 Jump to the net.
- ○ get
- ○ net
- ○ jump

4 The girl can run and kick.
- ○ girl
- ○ run
- ○ kick

5 The friend can jump.
- ○ can
- ○ jump
- ○ friend

Word Order

Read each group of words. Circle the group of words that are in an order that makes sense. Draw a line under each capital letter.

Words in a sentence must be in an order that makes sense.

1 The king is sad.

sad. king is The

2 the king Tell to come.

Tell the king to come.

3 bake Let's cake. him a

Let's bake him a cake.

4 Let's eat the cake.

eat Let's the cake.

Read the words.
Write them in order.

king   The   eats   cake   .

Word Order

These words are mixed up.
Put them in order.
Then write each sentence.

1 snow.   bear   likes   This

_____

- -

_____

2 water   cold.   The   is

_____

- -

_____

3 fast.   The   runs   bear

_____

- -

_____

4 play.   bears   Two

_____

- -

_____

Word Order

Read each group of words. Fill in the circle next to the words that are in an order that makes sense.

1
○ Pam will bake a cake.
○ bake Pam a will cake.
○ will Pam cake. a bake

2
○ duck. The king has a
○ The king has a duck.
○ has a king The duck.

3
○ The king will eat cake.
○ king will The cake. eat
○ cake. king will The eat

4
○ will king. the see Pam
○ king. Pam see will the
○ Pam will see the king.

5
○ lake. the in is The duck
○ The duck is in the lake.
○ The lake. duck in is the

6
○ Ramón will help Pam bake.
○ bake. Ramón help will Pam
○ Ramón bake. Pam will help

Capitalizing Titles

Circle all the words that are capitalized.

First words and important words in a title are capitalized.

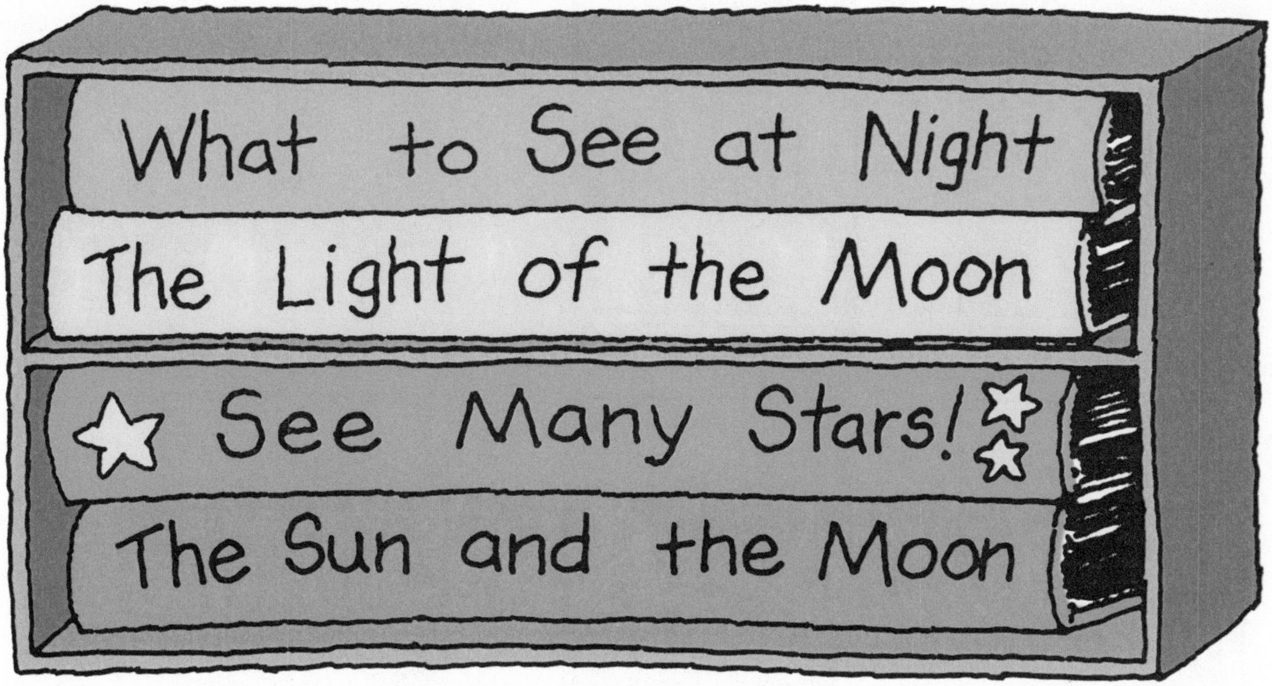

What to See at Night

The Light of the Moon

⭐ See Many Stars! ⭐⭐

The Sun and the Moon

Now use some of the words from the titles above to write your own titles.

_____

_____

_____

_____

Capitalizing Titles

Read the titles. Circle all the words that should be capitalized.

1. look at the stars!

2. the moon shines at night

3. we see planets

4. many moons shine

5. night and day

Read each set of titles. Draw a line under the correct title.

1. The Sun in the Sky

   the sun in the sky

2. See the stars!

   See the Stars!

Capitalizing Titles

Read the titles. Fill in the circle next to the title with the correct words capitalized.

1
○ Where is the Sun?
○ Where is the sun?
○ Where Is the Sun?

2
○ Day and Night
○ day And night
○ Day And Night

3
○ the Big Bad wolf
○ the big, bad wolf
○ The Big, Bad Wolf

4
○ many cats to see
○ Many cats To See
○ Many Cats to See

5
○ how many pigs?
○ How Many Pigs?
○ How many pigs?

6
○ Ant and Cricket Play
○ Ant and Cricket play
○ Ant And Cricket Play

Naming Words

Read each sentence. Draw a line under the word or words that name the person, place, animal, or thing in each sentence.

1 The pot is big.

2 See the top?

3 The pan is big.

4 Jim can mop.

- -

Draw a line from each sentence to the picture that shows the naming word in that sentence.

1 The pot is hot.

2 See the pan?

3 Jim is fast.

Naming Words

Circle the naming words in the sentences.

1 Jan can go in a van.

3 The van can go fast.

2 The van is on a hill.

4 Dan sees Jan.

Draw a picture of a person, place, animal, or thing.
Write a sentence about your picture. Circle the naming words.

Naming Words

Read each sentence. Fill in the circle next to the naming word.

1 See the hot pans?
- ○ hot
- ○ See
- ○ pans

2 See Jim mop fast.
- ○ fast
- ○ Jim
- ○ See

3 The rat hid.
- ○ The
- ○ rat
- ○ hid

4 The cat naps.
- ○ cat
- ○ The
- ○ naps

5 Can the cat see?
- ○ see
- ○ cat
- ○ Can

6 The puppy plays.
- ○ puppy
- ○ plays
- ○ The

Linking Verbs

Read each sentence. Draw a line under the linking verb <u>is</u>, <u>are</u>, <u>was</u>, or <u>were</u>.

Is, are, was, and *were* are linking verbs. *Is* tells about one. *Are* tells about more than one. *Was* tells about one in the past. *Were* tells about more than one in the past.

1 The hen is digging.

2 The pig was having fun.

3 The chicks were helping.

4 The cat and duck are playing.

· ·

Read each sentence. Circle <u>now</u> or <u>in the past</u> to show when it happens or happened.

1 The hen is planting.　　　　　now　　　in the past

2 The cat was not helping.　　　now　　　in the past

3 The chicks are with the hen.　now　　　in the past

Linking Verbs

Circle the linking verb. Write <u>now</u> or <u>past</u> to tell when the action happens or happened.

1 The chicks are eating.

2 The duck is swimming.

3 The cat was napping.

4 The pig is digging.

5 They were playing.

Linking Verbs

Fill in the circle next to the linking verb that completes each sentence.

1 The hen _____ sitting.
- ○ was
- ○ are
- ○ were

2 The pigs _____ digging.
- ○ was
- ○ is
- ○ are

3 The chicks _____ napping.
- ○ was
- ○ is
- ○ are

4 They _____ playing.
- ○ were
- ○ is
- ○ was

5 The duck _____ swimming.
- ○ were
- ○ is
- ○ are

6 The cat _____ meowing.
- ○ are
- ○ were
- ○ is

Capitalizing Names

Circle the special names in the picture.
Write each one correctly on a line.

Sometimes the names of people, places, animals, and things are special. They begin with a capital letter.

1 _____

2 _____

3 _____

4 _____

Capitalizing Names and First Words

Read the sentences.
Circle the words that are capitalized.

> The first word in a sentence starts with a capital letter. Words that name a special person, place, animal, or thing begin with a capital letter.

1. The goats have a problem.

2. They do not like the troll.

3. The troll's name is Nosey.

4. Nosey is big and bad.

. . . .

Draw a line to match each sentence to why the underlined word is capitalized.

1. Dan and <u>Pam</u> like the play.

2. <u>They</u> will read it to Jim.

First word in a sentence

Names a special person, place, animal, or thing.

Capitalizing Names and First Words

Read each sentence. Fill in the circle next to the word that needs a capital letter.

1 i like the goat named Gruff
- ○ Goats
- ○ The
- ○ I

2 I read the story with ron.
- ○ Read
- ○ Story
- ○ Ron

3 Little gruff had a problem.
- ○ Had
- ○ Gruff
- ○ Problem

4 a troll was on the bridge.
- ○ On
- ○ Bridge
- ○ A

5 The troll's name was nosey.
- ○ Name
- ○ Nosey
- ○ His

WRITING

That's Amazing!

Help the mouse through the maze by coloring each box with a word that begins with a capital letter.

A sentence begins with a **capital letter**.

The	For	That	with	know	but
here	on	When	Have	next	we
as	after	good	Make	there	see
Go	Look	Are	Could	is	why
This	who	said	in	come	them
Has	Name	Before	Her	Where	The

 Read the back of a cereal box. How many capital letters did you find? Write the number next to the cheese.

Squeak!

Circle the words that show the correct way to begin each sentence.

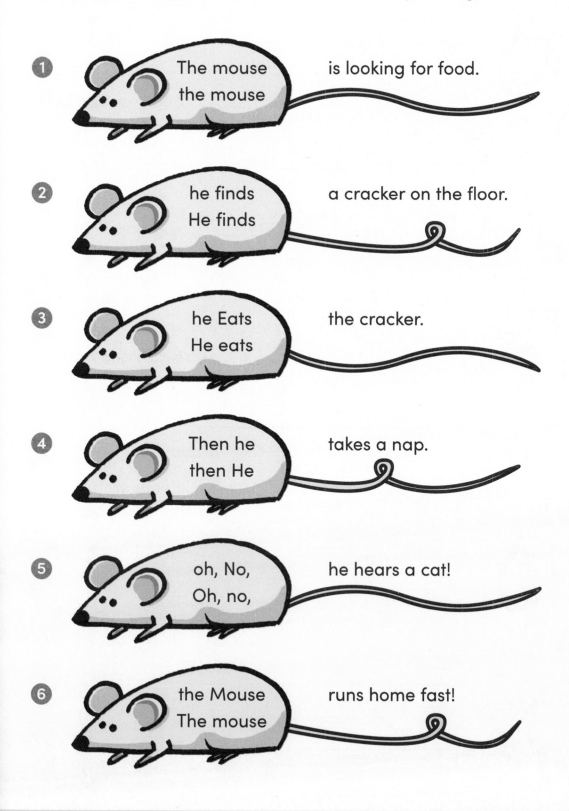

1 The mouse
   the mouse
   is looking for food.

2 he finds
   He finds
   a cracker on the floor.

3 he Eats
   He eats
   the cracker.

4 Then he
   then He
   takes a nap.

5 oh, No,
   Oh, no,
   he hears a cat!

6 the Mouse
   The mouse
   runs home fast!

Counting Sheep

Write the beginning words correctly to make a sentence.

1 we read
_____
_____ books before bed.

2 then we
_____
_____ hug good night.

3 my bed
_____
_____ is soft and cozy.

4 my cat
_____
_____ sleeps with me.

5 the sky
_____
_____ has turned dark.

6 my eyes
_____
_____ close.

Sweet Dreams!

Write each beginning correctly to make a sentence.

1 my dog
_____
- -
_____ runs in her sleep.

2 she must
_____
- -
_____ be dreaming.

3 maybe she
_____
- -
_____ is chasing a cat.

4 sometimes she
_____
- -
_____ even barks.

5 i think
_____
- -
_____ it is funny.

On another sheet of paper, write a sentence about a dream you remember. Circle the capital letter at the beginning of your sentence.

The Night Sky

Add a period to each sentence.

1. Many things shine in the sky at night__

2. The moon looks the brightest__

3. It is closest to Earth__

4. The stars look like tiny dots__

5. They are very far away__

6. The sun is a star__

7. Planets look like colored stars__

8. Their light does not twinkle__

9. Shooting stars look like stars that are falling__

10. There are many things to see in the night sky__

© Scholastic Inc.

Twinkle, Twinkle, Little Star

Rewrite each sentence using periods.

1 Tonight I saw a star

_____

- - - - - - - - - - - - - - - - - - -

_____

2 I saw the star twinkle

_____

- - - - - - - - - - - - - - - - - - -

_____

3 It looked like a candle

_____

- - - - - - - - - - - - - - - - - - -

_____

4 It was very bright

_____

- - - - - - - - - - - - - - - - - - -

_____

5 I made a wish

_____

- - - - - - - - - - - - - - - - - - -

_____

6 I hope it comes true

_____

- - - - - - - - - - - - - - - - - - -

_____

Hop to It!

Rewrite each sentence correctly.

A **telling sentence** begins with a **capital letter** and ends with a **period**.

1 frogs and toads lay eggs

_____

- -

_____

2 the eggs are in the water

_____

- -

_____

3 tadpoles hatch from the eggs

_____

- -

_____

4 the tadpoles grow legs

_____

- -

_____

5 the tadpoles lose their tales

_____

- -

_____

Hop to It Some More!

Rewrite each sentence correctly.

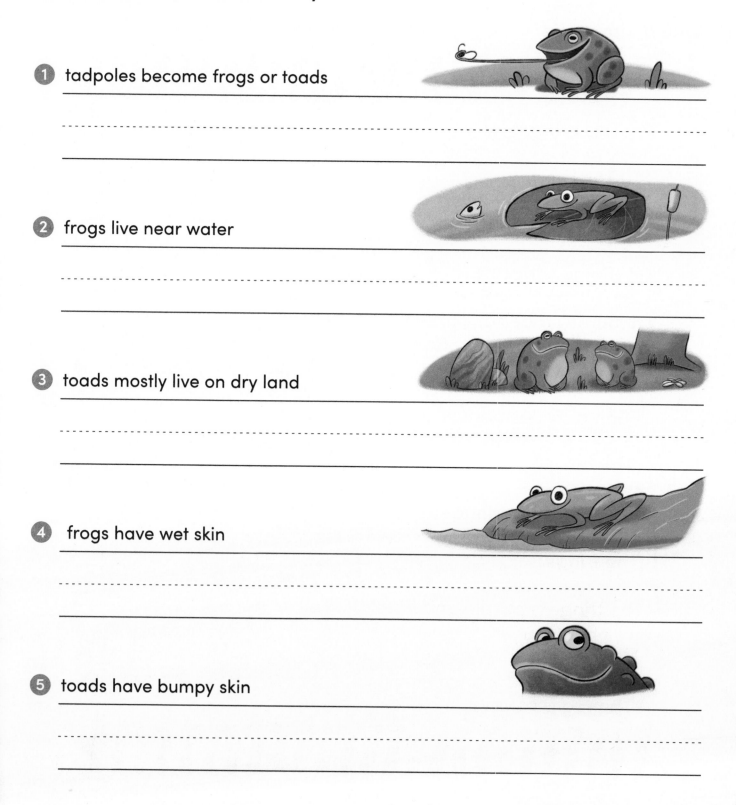

1 tadpoles become frogs or toads

_____

- -

_____

2 frogs live near water

_____

- -

_____

3 toads mostly live on dry land

_____

- -

_____

4 frogs have wet skin

_____

- -

_____

5 toads have bumpy skin

_____

- -

_____

Striped Sentences

A **sentence** tells a complete idea. It should always make sense.

Color the rug to show:

GREEN = sentence   **YELLOW** = not a sentence

This is a rug.
The rug
The rug has stripes.
Some stripes
Some stripes are green.
Some stripes
Some stripes are yellow.
The rug
The rug has a fringe.
The fringe
The fringe is purple and blue.
The rug is
The rug is colorful.

High-Flying Sentences

Color each flag that tells a complete thought. Leave the other flags blank.

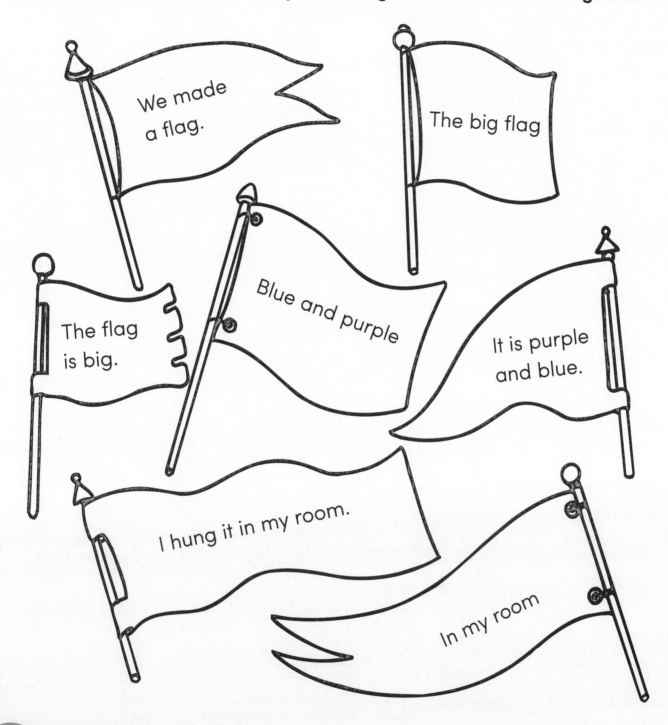

We made a flag.

The big flag

The flag is big.

Blue and purple

It is purple and blue.

I hung it in my room.

In my room

⭐ On another sheet of paper, turn this into a sentence: The biggest flag.

At the Seashore

Unscramble the words to make a sentence.
Write the new sentence below each picture.

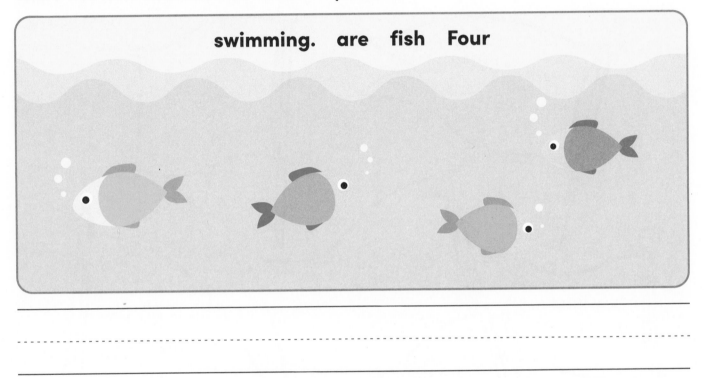

swimming. are fish Four

_____

- -

one have We shovel.

_____

- -

In the Rain Forest

Unscramble the words to make a sentence.
Write the new sentence. Do not forget to put a period at the end.

1 A hiding jaguar is

_____

- -

_____

2 blue Some butterflies are

_____

- -

_____

3 water in jump the Frogs

_____

- -

_____

4 snakes trees Green hang from

_____

- -

_____

5 very tall grow The trees

_____

- -

_____

⭐ Scramble a sentence for someone at home.
Be sure the first word begins with a capital letter.

Snakes Alive!

Color the snake that tells the naming part in
each sentence below.

A sentence
has a **naming
part.** It tells
who or what
the sentence
is about.

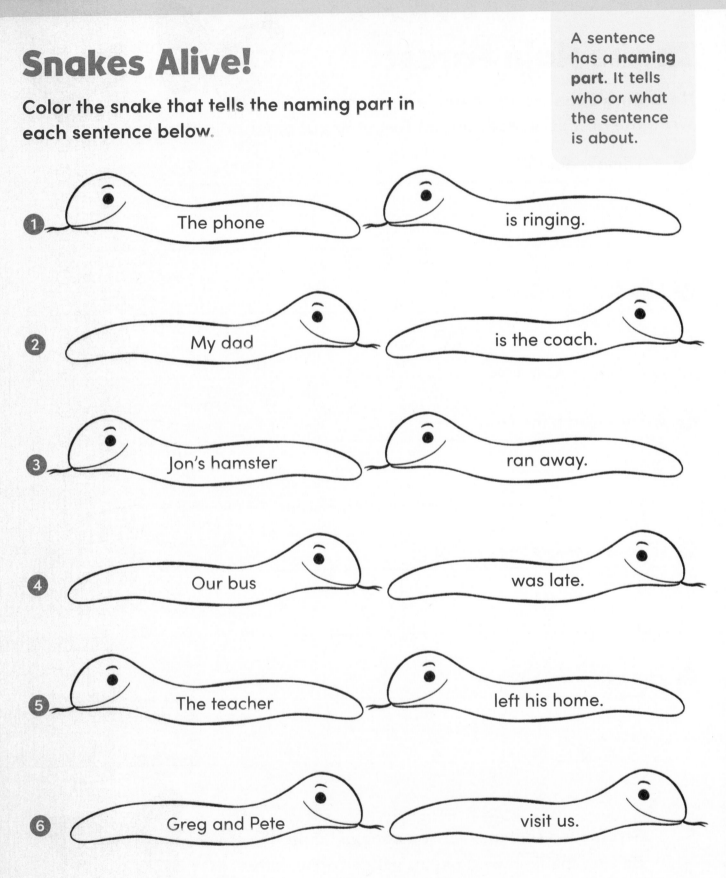

1. The phone — is ringing.

2. My dad — is the coach.

3. Jon's hamster — ran away.

4. Our bus — was late.

5. The teacher — left his home.

6. Greg and Pete — visit us.

Slithering Sentences

Circle the naming part in each sentence below.
Then color the picture to match.

1. The blue snakes are playing.

2. The yellow snake is climbing a tree.

3. The green snake hides under a rock.

4. The brown snake is swimming.

5. The red snake is hanging on a branch.

6. The purple snake sleeps in a tree.

7. The black snake rests on a rock.

8. The orange snake is near an egg.

Who Is That?

The **naming part** of a sentence can be a person.

Use the pictures to find naming parts to make each sentence complete.

1. ______________________ fell on the ice.

2. ______________________ ran in the race.

3. ______________________ went inside the dark cave.

4. ______________________ climbed the hill.

5. ______________________ swam across the pool.

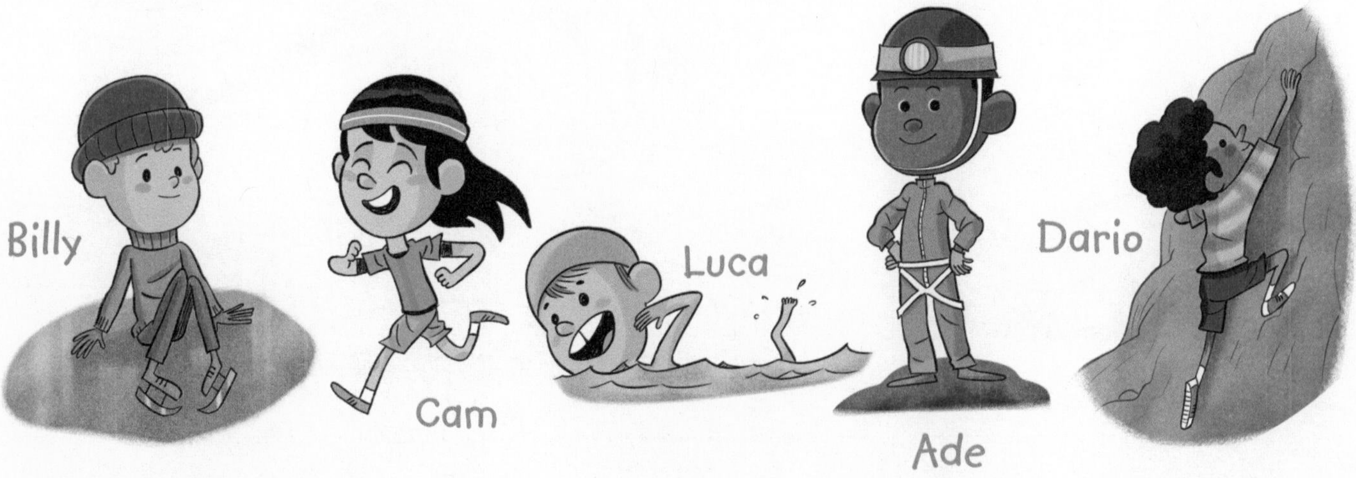

Billy
Cam
Luca
Ade
Dario

Where Is That?

Use naming parts to complete each sentence
that tells about the map.

The **naming part** of
a sentence can be a
place or thing.

Tree Lane

1 _____
- -
_____ is near the swings

2 _____
- -
_____ is far from the cave.

3 _____
- -
_____ is a good place to fish.

4 _____
- -
_____ has bats inside.

5 _____
- -
_____ is along Tree Lane.

Vacation Photos

Use naming parts to write a complete sentence about each picture.

_____

- - - - - - - - - - - - - - - - - -

_____

- - - - - - - - - - - - - - - - - -

_____

_____

- - - - - - - - - - - - - - - - - -

_____

- - - - - - - - - - - - - - - - - -

_____

More Vacation Photos

Use naming parts to write a complete sentence about each picture.

No Bones About It!

A sentence has an **action part**. It tells what is happening.

Color the bone that tells the action part in each sentence below.

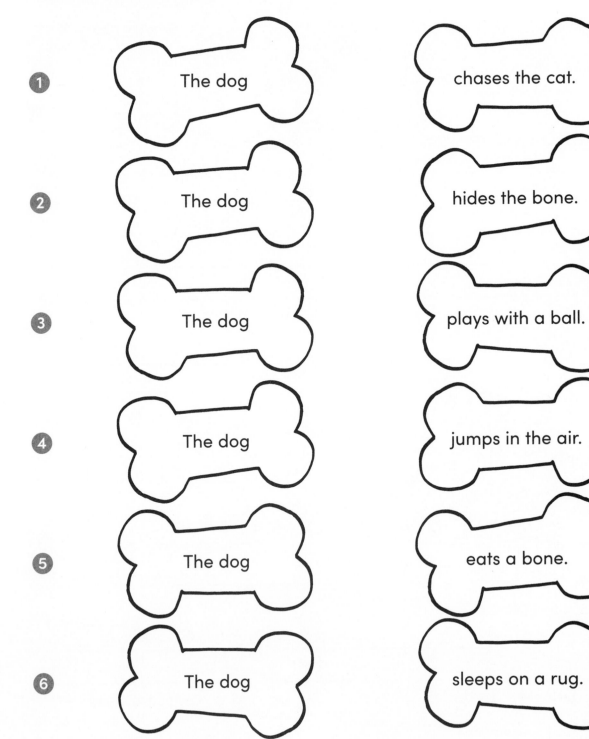

1 The dog   chases the cat.

2 The dog   hides the bone.

3 The dog   plays with a ball.

4 The dog   jumps in the air.

5 The dog   eats a bone.

6 The dog   sleeps on a rug.

Mighty Good Sentences

Choose the ending that tells what each dog is doing.
Remember to use periods.

| is eating. |
| is sleeping. |
| is jumping. |
| is playing. |

1 The white dog _____

2 The gray dog _____

3 The spotted dog _____

4 The striped dog _____

⭐ On another sheet of paper, draw another dog and write a sentence about it.

A Busy Classroom

The action part of a sentence is called the **verb**.

Complete each sentence with an action verb to tell what is happening in the picture. Remember to use periods.

_____
- -

1 Mr. Downs _____

_____
- -

2 The fish _____

_____
- -

3 James _____

_____
- -

4 Cara _____

Pencil It In

Choose a verb from the Word Bank
to complete each sentence.

Sometimes the
verb does not
show action. It
still tells what is
happening.

For example:
I **know** the answer.
I **am** hungry.

Word Bank

seems	am	gets	were
is	are	was	eat

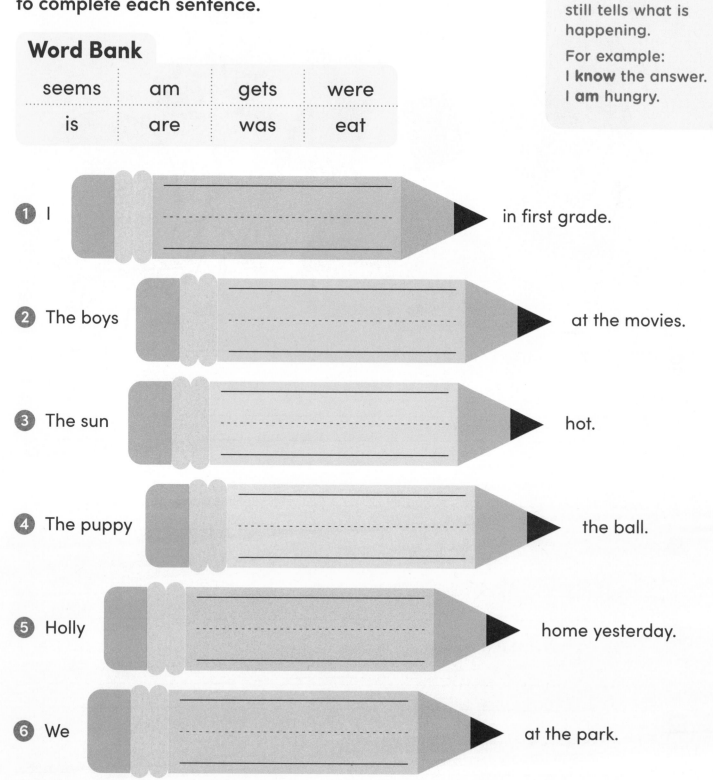

1 I _____ in first grade.

2 The boys _____ at the movies.

3 The sun _____ hot.

4 The puppy _____ the ball.

5 Holly _____ home yesterday.

6 We _____ at the park.

Topsy-Turvy!

A sentence has a verb that tells what is happening.

Write five sentences that tell what is happening in the pictures.

1 _____

2 _____

3 _____

4 _____

5 _____

What Is Going On?

Look around you. Write four sentences that tell what is happening.

1 _____

2 _____

3 _____

4 _____

The Caboose

In each caboose, draw a picture to show where each sentence takes place.

A sentence is more interesting when it tells **where** the action is happening.

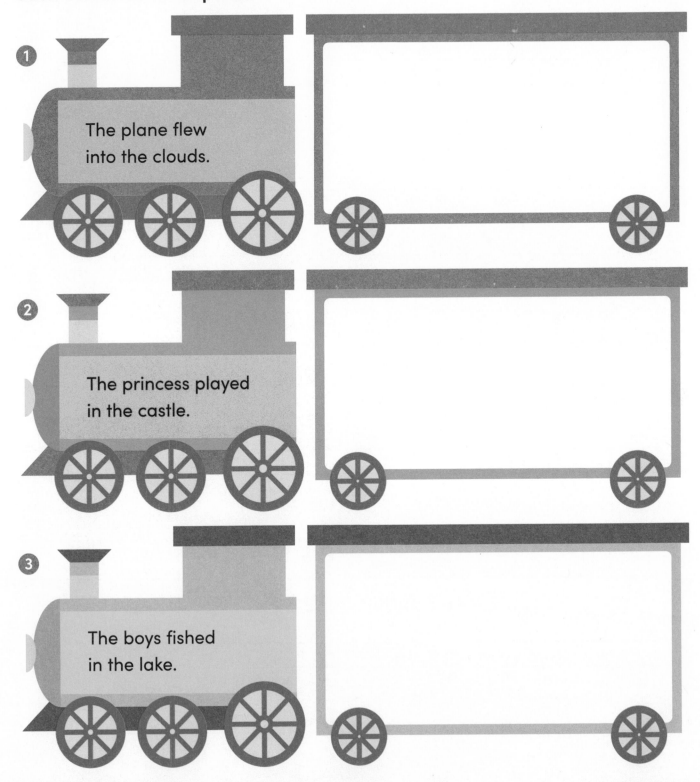

1. The plane flew into the clouds.

2. The princess played in the castle.

3. The boys fished in the lake.

© Scholastic Inc.

When Was That?

Circle the part that tells when in each sentence.

A sentence may also tell **when** the action takes place.

1 George Washington lived long ago.

2 The mail carrier was late yesterday.

3 The bear slept in winter.

4 We are going to the zoo today.

5 The leaves change in the fall.

6 I lost my tooth last night.

7 It rained all day.

8 The party starts at noon.

9 We got home yesterday.

10 We ate turkey on Thanksgiving Day.

11 The kitten was playing this morning.

12 Tomorrow I am going to my grandmother's house.

Chugging Along

Write an ending for each sentence that tells where
or when the action takes place.

naming part	the action	where or when

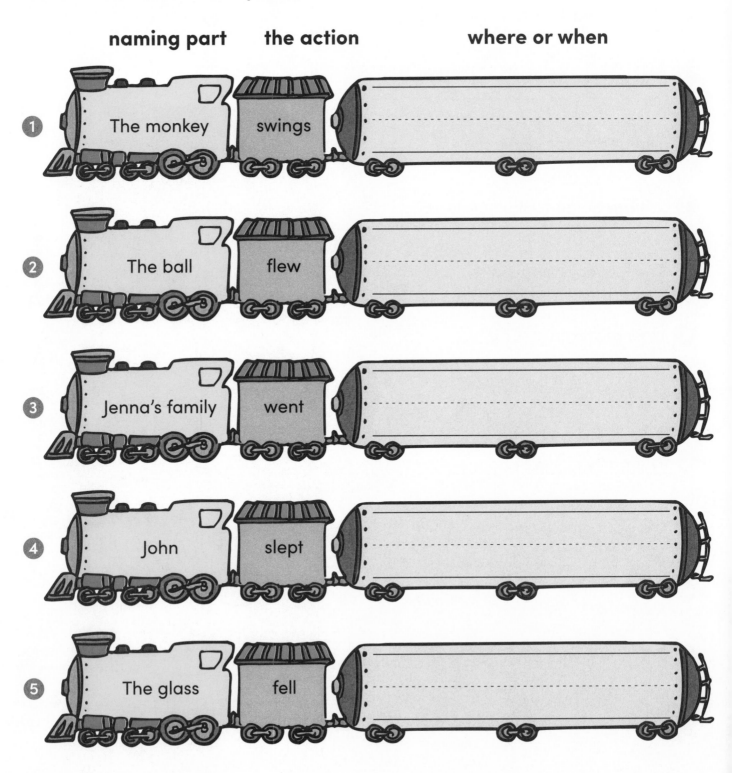

1. The monkey | swings
2. The ball | flew
3. Jenna's family | went
4. John | slept
5. The glass | fell

My Busy Day

Write the beginning part of each sentence to tell about your day.
Draw a picture to match each sentence.

_____

this morning.

_____

this afternoon.

_____

tonight.

⭐ On another sheet of paper, write four sentences and draw four pictures
to tell about your best day ever.

Silly Sentences

Complete each missing part to make silly sentences.

A sentence may have three parts: **a naming part, an action,** and a part that tells **where or when.**

the naming part	the action	where or when
1 The monkey		on his head.
2 My dad	is hopping	
3	flipped	in the forest.
4	bounced	
5 My shoes		at the pool.
6 The snake	twisted	
7 The bubbles	filled	

On another sheet of paper, write a new sentence by scrambling the three parts listed above. For example, use the naming part in #1, the action part in #2, and the where or when part from #3. Draw a picture of your sentence.

Sweet Sentences

Use choices from each part to make three "sweet" sentences.

naming part	action	where or when
I	ate doughnuts	at the bakery
She	ate candy	at the party
He	chewed gum	at the park

Home Sweet Home

Write three sentences about the picture.
For example: The dog is sleeping outside.

1 _____

2 _____

3 _____

The Construction Crew

Write three sentences
about the picture.
Include three parts
in each sentence.

1

2

3

Mystery Boxes

Read the describing words to guess the mystery object. Use the words in the Word Bank.

Describing words help you imagine how something looks, feels, smells, sounds, or tastes. Describing words are called **adjectives**.

Word Bank

| ball | bat | silly | blanket | cracker |

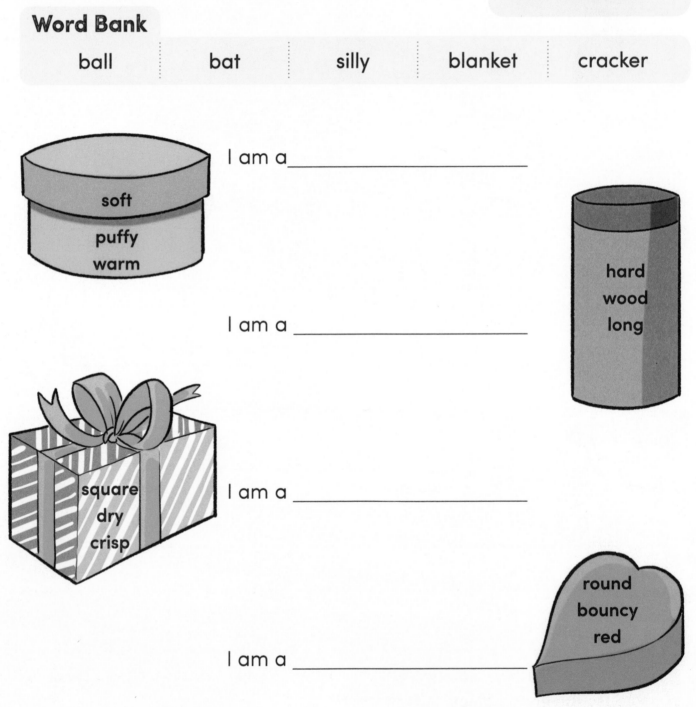

soft
puffy
warm

I am a _____

hard
wood
long

I am a _____

square
dry
crisp

I am a _____

round
bouncy
red

I am a _____

Sensational Words

Choose words from the Word Bank to describe each picture.

It tastes _____.

It looks _____.

It feels _____.

Word Bank
bumpy
crunchy
furry
gray
red
salty
smooth
squeaky
sweet

It feels _____.

It tastes _____.

It sounds _____.

It looks _____.

It sounds _____.

It feels _____.

 Find two objects outside. On another sheet of paper, write two adjectives to describe each object.

More Describing Words

How would you describe a lollipop or a baby chick? Complete the chart below with describing words for each. Choose words from the Word Bank.

Word Bank

thin	thick	smooth	bumpy	fuzzy
soft	hard	fluffy	shiny	sticky

Lollipop    Chick

_____   _____

_____   _____

_____   _____

_____   _____

1 Name something that is thin. _____

2 Name something that is thick. _____

3 Name something that is bumpy. _____

Pretty Packages

Write three words to describe each gift.
Then color them to match.

The describing words in a
sentence help the reader paint
a picture in his or her mind.

_____ (color)

_____ (color)

_____ (pattern)

_____ (color)

_____ (color)

_____ (pattern)

_____ (color)

_____ (color)

_____ (pattern)

_____ (color)

_____ (color)

_____ (pattern)

What's Inside?

Use describing words to write a sentence about each package.
For example: I found a swimsuit in the **red and yellow** package.

1 I found _____ in the _____ package.

2 I found _____ in the _____ package.

3 I found _____ in the _____ package.

4 I found _____ in the _____ package.

A Walk in the Park

Write describing words to finish each sentence.

> Describing words make a sentence more interesting.

1 A _____ duck is

_____

swimming in the _____ pond.

2 A _____ man is walking

_____

his _____ dog.

3 A _____ girl is

_____

flying a _____ kite.

4 A _____ woman is sitting

_____

on a _____ .

Around Town

Write a sentence for each picture. Use the describing word in the sentence.

large

_____

_____

----

beautiful

_____

_____

----

crowded

_____

_____

----

noisy

_____

_____

Keep It in Order

Finish each story by writing sentences about the last pictures.

Sentences can be written in order to tell a story.

1

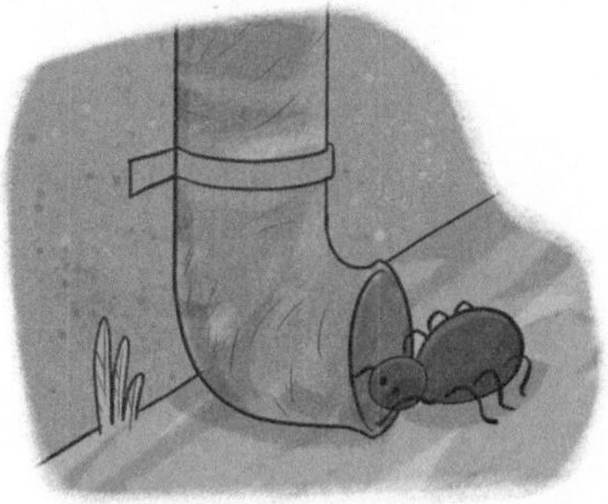

2

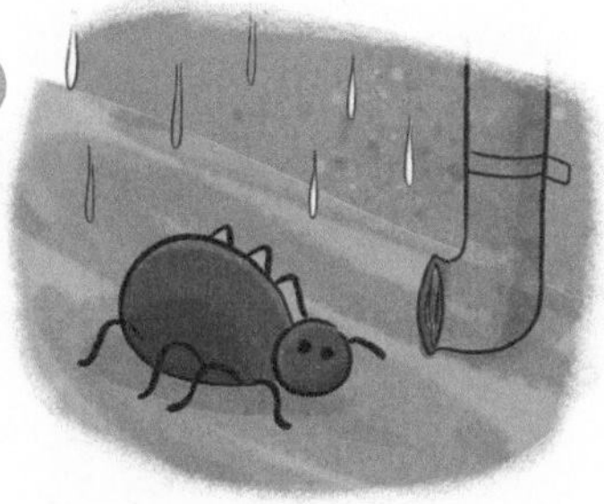

3

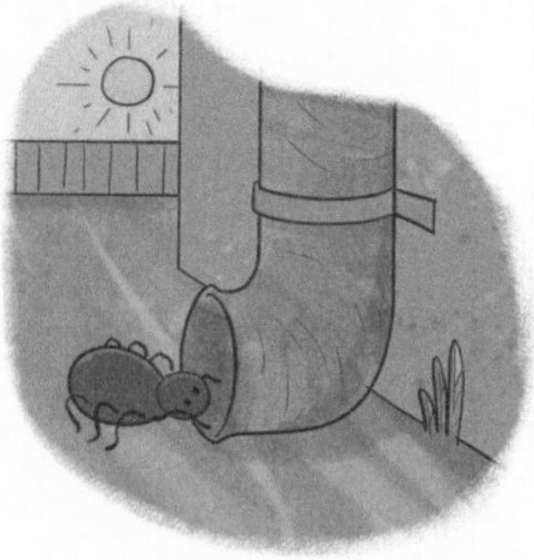

First, the spider crawls up.

Next,

Last,

1

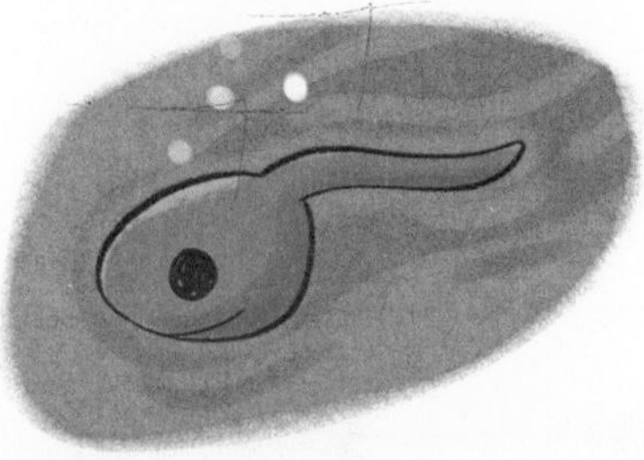

2

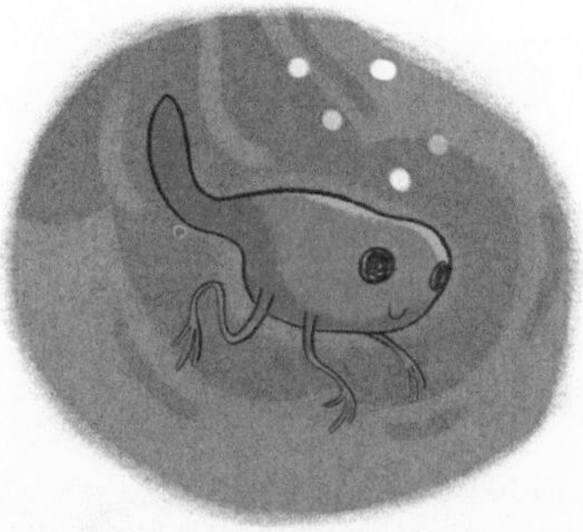

3

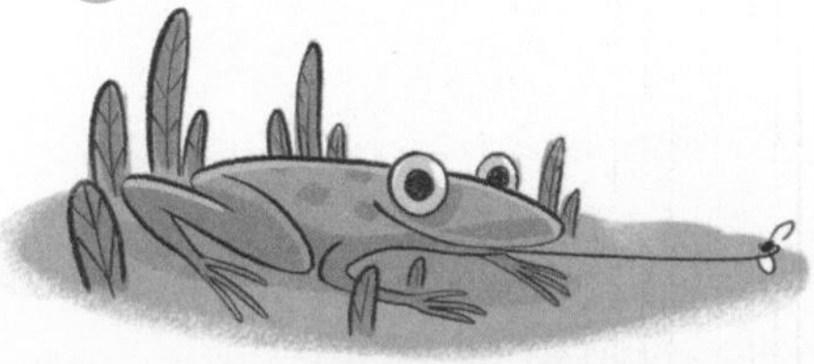

First, there is a tadpole.

Next,

Last,

What's Next?

Finish each set of directions by writing sentences about the last pictures.

Sentences can be written in order to give directions.

①  ②  ③

First, _mix all the ingredients._

Next, _____

Last, _____

First, _put your dog in the tub._

Next, _____

Last, _____

Which Title Fits?

Match each title with its story.
Write the title above the picture.

The name of a story is called the **title**. It matches with the story. Most of the words in a title begin with capital letters.

A Big Beak	The Big Win
My Space Friend	A Knight's Tale

(title) _____

(title) _____

(title) _____

(title) _____

A Terrific Title

Fill in the missing words to make your own story. Then write a title that fits with your story. Draw a picture about your story in the box.

_____
(title)

One _____ day,

_____ took his pet

_____ for a walk. First,

they went to the _____

Then they walked to _____'s

house. Last, they went home to _____

_____. It was a

_____ day!

Story Strips

Write a sentence to tell about each part of the story. Remember to give the story a title.

Beginning

_____
(title)

Middle

End

More Story Strips

Think of a story you know well. Write about the beginning, middle, and end parts. Draw pictures to match. Be sure to give your story a title.

_____

(title)

Beginning

Middle

End

What Is a Map?

Look at the picture of the playground. It is a picture taken from the above. It shows all the things in the playground you can play with.

Circle the name of each item you see in the picture.

swing   merry-go-round

seesaw   umbrella

slide   bench

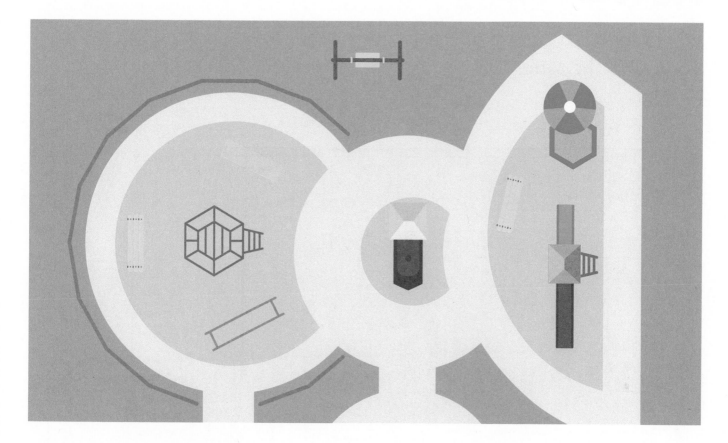

Now look at the map of the same playground. A map is a drawing of a place. It shows where things are. A map shows how a place looks from above.

1 How is the map like the picture? _____

_____

2 How are the map and picture different? _____

_____

3 Circle all the things you see in both the picture and the map.

swing   seesaw   slide   merry-go-round   umbrella   bench

Make a Map

Remember, a map is a drawing of a place. Look at the map of Jason's bedroom. The map shows where things are in his bedroom.

Jason's Bedroom

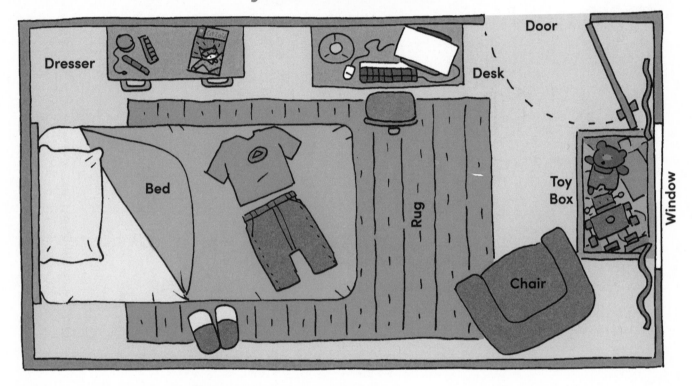

Circle the words that tell where things are.

1 The bed is on the _____.

    dresser   rug

2 The toy box is next to the _____.

    window   desk

Now think about your own bedroom. Where is your bed?
Where is your door? What else is in your bedroom?

Draw a map of your bedroom in the box below.
Remember to write a title for your map.

_____

Title

A Picture of Earth

Earth is the planet we live on. Look at the picture of Earth below. The picture was taken from space. You can see that Earth is round like a ball. The large blue areas are oceans. An **ocean** is a large body of water. The orange and green areas are land.

Finish each sentence with a word from the word bank.

Word Bank

round   water   Earth

1 We live on a planet called

_____.

2 Earth's shape is

_____.

3 There is less land on Earth than

_____.

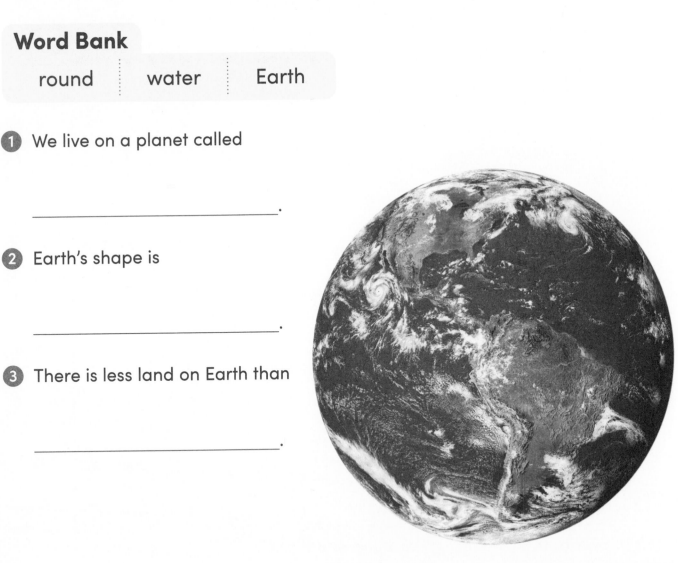

What Is a Globe?

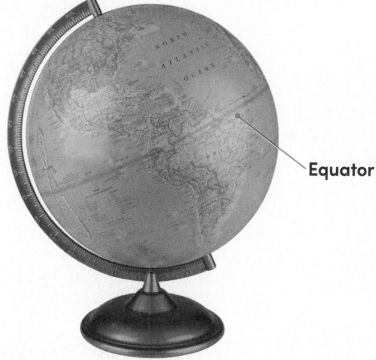

Equator

Globe

A **globe** is a model of Earth. It is round like Earth. A globe shows Earth's land and water.

The **equator** is a line around the middle of the globe. It divides Earth into two equal parts: North and South.

....

Circle the correct answer for each question.

1 What is a globe?

a photo of Earth   a model of Earth

2 What does a globe show?

land and water   people and homes

3 How does the equator divide Earth?

into four equal parts   into two equal parts

Maps and Globes

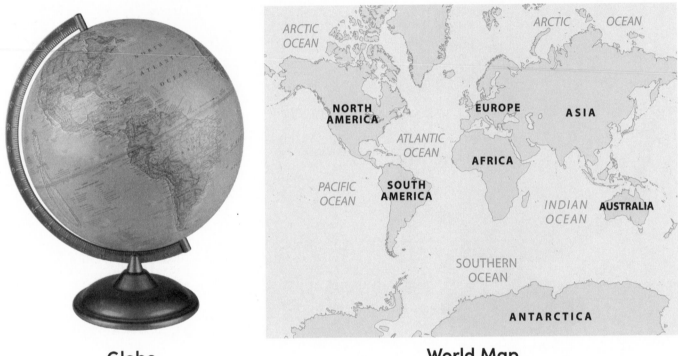

Globe   World Map

Maps and globes help us learn about Earth. Remember, a globe is round like Earth. You can only see half of Earth at one time on a globe.

A map is a drawing of a place. Maps are flat. A world map shows all of Earth at once. It makes it easy to find places all over Earth.

· ·

Draw a line under each true sentence.

1 A globe shows only half of Earth at one time.

2 A map is the same shape as a globe.

3 You can see all of Earth at the same time on a map.

Look at the globe on the previous page. Now look at the map on this page. What land on Earth do you see on both the map and globe?

Look at the map below. Now, compare it to the globe on page 216. What land and water can you see on the map below that you can also see on the globe? Color the land green. Color the water blue. Then, color the land you cannot see on the globe gray. Color the water you cannot see light blue.

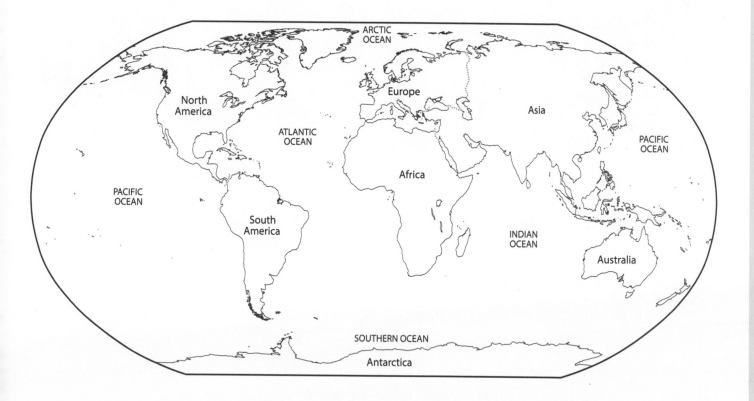

Big and Small Places

Parker School Playground

Swings

Slide

Climbing Bars

Sandbox

Map 1

Parker School Grounds

Playground

Trees

School

Parking Lot

Sidewalk

Map 2

You know that a map is a drawing of a place that shows where things are located. Did you know that you can make a map of any place? Maps can show big places and small places.

Tanya is Jason's cousin. She goes to the Parker School. Map 1 shows the school playground. Map 2 shows whole school grounds.

Draw a line under the sentences that are true.

 The playground has a seesaw.

 The school is bigger than the trees.

3 The school has a parking lot.

Tanya's Neighborhood

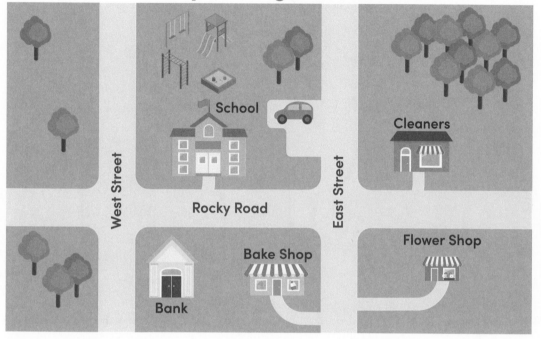

Map 3

The map on this page shows Tanya's neighborhood.
It shows the location of the Parker School.

Use the maps to answer the questions.

1 What is the biggest building
in Tanya's Neighborhood? _____

2 What is the smallest building
in Tanya's Neighborhood? _____

3 Look at all three maps.
Which map shows the biggest area? _____

4 Which of the three maps
shows the smallest area? _____

Near or Far?

Maps can show you whether things are near or far away. Something that is near is close to you. Something that is far is a long way from you.

Circle the word that correctly answers the question.

1 Is Jason near or far from the ball?

2 Find the bench. Is it near or far from the ball?

3 Is the sandbox near or far from the ball?

⭐ Look around your room. What things are near to you? What things are far from you?

This is a map of Jason's neighborhood. Some places are near his house. Other places are far away.

Jason's Neighborhood

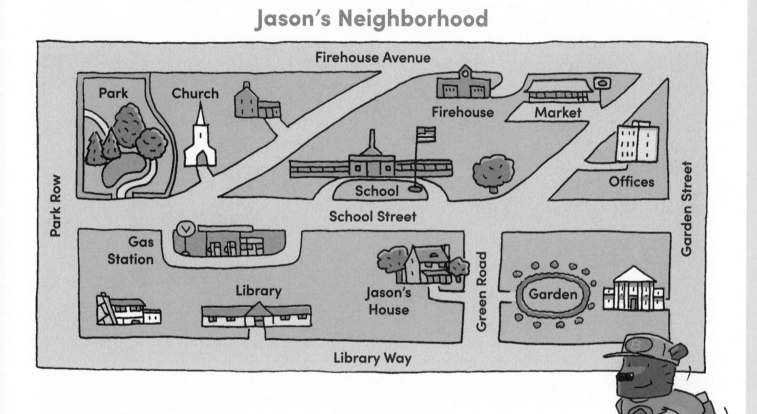

Circle the word that tells which is nearer to Jason's house.

1. firehouse or school

2. library or park

Draw a line under the word that tells which is farther away from Jason's house.

3. library or firehouse

4. market or park

5. offices or garden

6. school or church

Left or Right?

Jason is visiting the Animal Park. He is trying to decide which direction to walk. Directions tell us which way we want to go. Many kinds of unusual animals live in the Animal Park. Using the directions left and right will make it easy for Jason to find them. Look at the drawing of Jason. He is facing forward. You are facing the same direction. Put an ✗ on his left side put a ✓ on his right side.

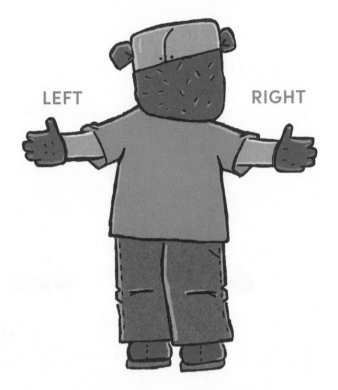

LEFT   RIGHT

Look at the map on page 223. Write the direction word left or right to tell which way Jason should walk to get from animal to animal.

1 🦓 to 🐅 _____

2 🦁 to 🦒 _____

3 🐘 to 🐘 _____

Face the front of your home. Raise your right hand. Then raise your left hand. Now face the back of your home. Are your right and left hands in the same place?

Look at the location of each animal to answer the questions.

1 Put an ✘ on the animal that is farther left.

red elephant   **green elephant**

2 Circle the animal that is nearer to the right.

bears   **camel**

Four Main Directions

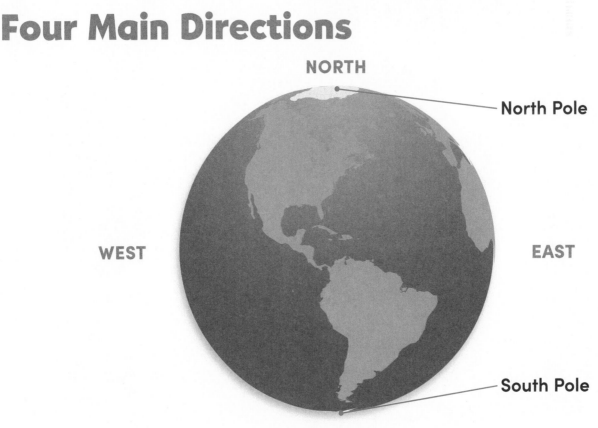

Earth has four main directions. They are north, south, east, and west. You can see them on this drawing. **North** is the direction toward the North Pole. **South** is the direction toward the South Pole.

Now find east. When you face north, **east** is always to your right. **West** is always to your left.

Write the direction word north **or** south **to answer the questions below.**

1 If you are facing south, what direction is behind you? _____

2 If you are facing east, what direction is to your left? _____

3 If you are facing west, what direction is to your left? _____

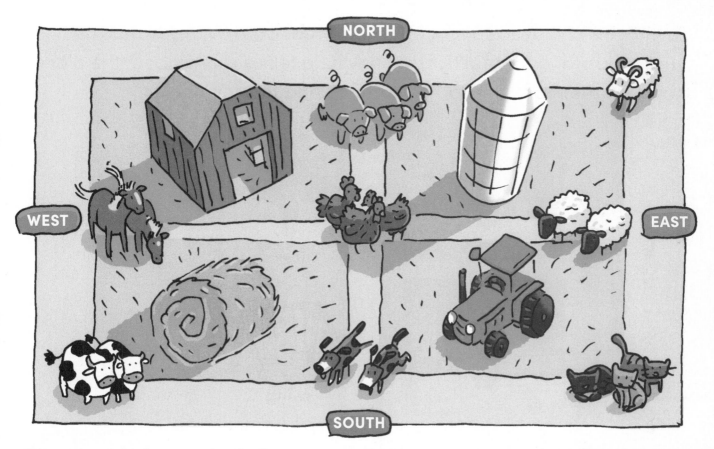

Directions help you find places on a map. You can see that the sheep are in the east. Circle them. On what side of the farm are the pigs?

Write the direction word that tells which way to go to get from animal to animal.

1	🐷	to 🐕	_____
2	🐐	to 🐑	_____
3	🐔	to 🐷	_____

Word Bank

north

south

east

west

What Are Map Symbols?

A **symbol** is a drawing that stands for a real thing. Many maps use symbols to stand for real things. They help tell us more about the place shown on the map. Look at the pictures and their symbols.

tree

swing

Look at the picture of the slide and the bench.
Draw your own symbol for each. Add a label for each symbol.

A map key tells you what the symbols on a map mean. Look at the map key and the map. Find the symbols in the key on the map.

Forest Park

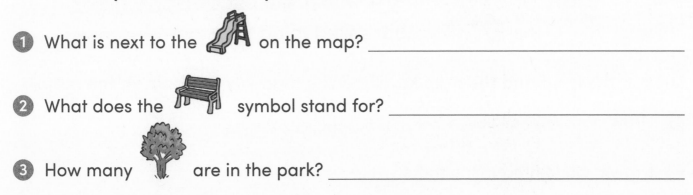

MAP KEY

tree · slide · bench · swing

Use the map to answer the questions.

1 What is next to the ⬛ on the map? _____

2 What does the ⬛ symbol stand for? _____

3 How many ⬛ are in the park? _____

Use Map Symbols

Lake View Park

Jason went to the park. He saw 🌲. He saw 🪨.
Then he saw a big 🫘. Jason put his toy boat into
the 🫘. The boat sailed to an 🌳.

Look at the map and the map key. Find the map key symbols on the map.

1 Draw an ✕ on the lake.

2 Draw a circle around the rocks.

3 Draw a ✓ on the trees.

Suppose you were asked to help remake Lake View Park. Think of three things you would add to the park to make it more fun. Draw them on the unfinished map of Lake View Park. Then add them to the Map Key. Some things on the Map Key are missing from the map. Add in the missing items in a new location.

Lake View Park

MAP KEY

lake   island   picnic table   tent

logs

A Neighborhood Map

Jason's Neighborhood

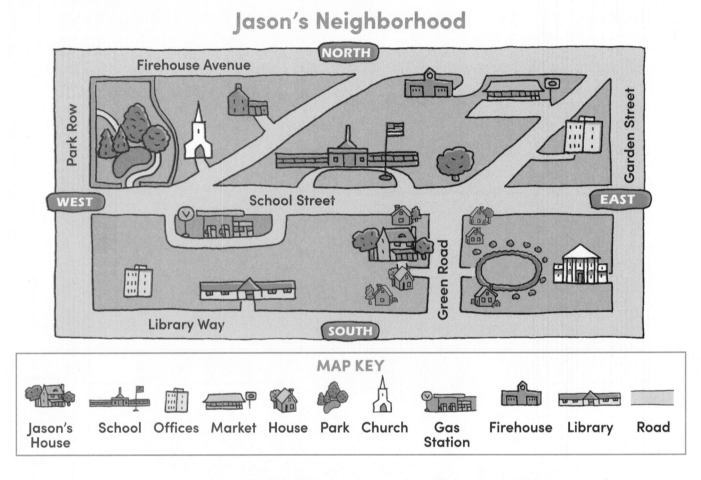

Here we are in Jason's neighborhood again. This time the map has a key to tell you what the symbols stand for. Follow Jason's route from his house to school. A **route** is a way to go from one place to another. Jason leaves his house and turns north on Green Road, then west on School Street. Use a black crayon to draw Jason's route.

There are other routes that Jason could take to get to school. Use a different color crayon to trace each route below.

1 Jason turns south on Green Road and west on Library Way.

2 Jason turns south on Green Road and east on Library Way.

Jason's house has an address. So does yours. An **address** has a number and a street name. Find the gas station on the map. The address of the gas station is 12 School Street.

Jason's Address

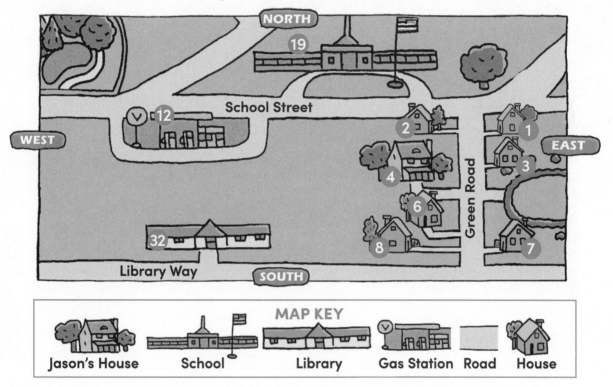

Use the map on this page to answer the questions below.

1 Draw a ✓ on the school. What is its address?

_____

2 Circle the library. What is its address?

_____

3 Draw a ★ on Jason's house. What is his address?

_____

Follow the Treasure!

This morning, Jason went up to the attic to look through some of the trunks stored there. At first, all he found were lots of old pictures and costumes. He was about to go down for lunch when he spotted a small trunk in the corner. He decided to open it. In the bottom of the trunk, he found clues that led to a treasure! Jason decided to skip lunch and begin his search right away.

Look at the treasure clues at the bottom of the next page. Follow the route Jason took. Use a crayon to trace the route along the map (on this page and the next), and find the treasure.

To Treasure of the Wind

- Begin in the west at the 🪨.
- Walk south then east to Blue Lake.
- Cross the 🪜 onto the 🪨.
- Go up the hill then east until you reach a 🪨.
- Take 10 giant steps south to the 🌳.
- Reach into the hole for the treasure.

Treasure Map

Dear Friends,

Let's make a treasure map together! I think our 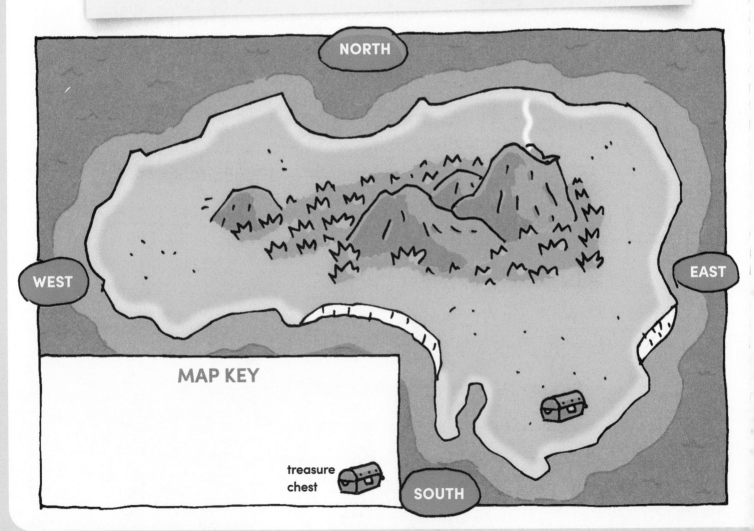 should be on an island. Now the rest is up to you. Decide what places to put on the island. Then draw symbols for them. Remember to show and label your symbols on the map key. Finally show a starting place. Use a crayon to trace a route to the 🧰.

Your friend,

Jason

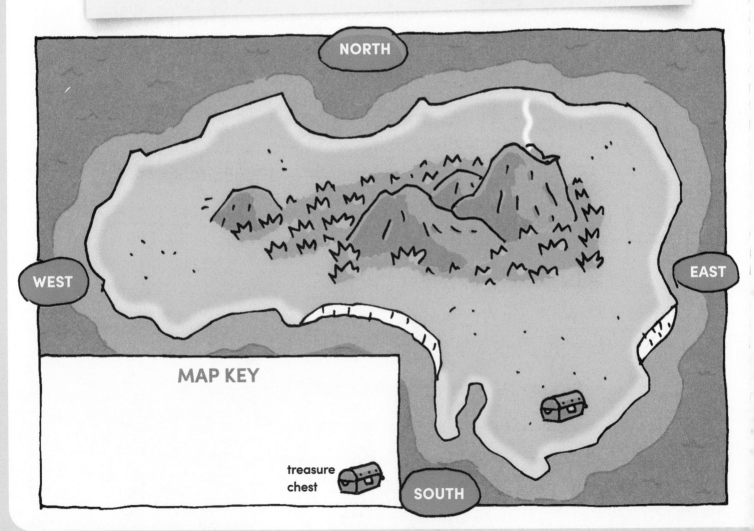

Let's Visit the Sea Park

Sea Park

Pretend you and your family are visiting the Sea Park.
Follow the directions below to trace a route through the park.

1 Go east from the Gate. Stop to buy tickets.
Then go north to the first show. Circle it.

2 Go north to the next animal attraction. Draw a ✔ on it.

3 Head to the picnic tables. Turn and go north to see the next show.
Draw a ★ on it.

4 Go east. Draw a line under the next show you see.

5 Go south past the hot dog stand. Then go west to the trash can.
Now go south. What show will you see? Draw an ✘ on it.

Land and Water

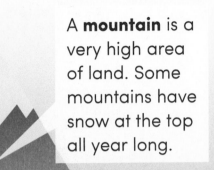

A **mountain** is a very high area of land. Some mountains have snow at the top all year long.

A **river** is a long body of water that flows across the land. A river usually flows into a lake or an ocean.

An **ocean** is a very large body of water. The water in an ocean is salty.

Earth has many different kinds of land and water.
Look at the picture above. Read the description for each kind of land and water. Which have you seen before?

Look at the picture. Then answer the questions.

1 How are the mountain and hill alike?

_____

2 How are they different?

_____

A **lake** is a body of water with land all around it. Most lakes have fresh water (water that is not salty).

A **hill** is land that is higher than the land around it. A hill is lower than a mountain.

A **plain** is flat land. Most plains are good for growing food.

Use the picture and descriptions to answer the questions.

1. I'm the highest land on Earth. What am I?

   plain   mountain

2. I'm a body of water surrounded by land. What am I?

   lake   plain

3. I flow across the land. What am I?

   river   lake

Land and Water on a Map

Frog Lake

Land and water can be shown as symbols on a map. Some symbols are colors. Water is usually shown as the color ▇. Describe the symbol for a lake in the map above.

Use the map to answer the questions.

1 What is the symbol for mountain? Draw a ★ on it on the map.

2 What does this symbol stand for 🏞️ ? _____
Draw a ✓ on it on the map.

3 Find the river on the map. Draw an ✗ on it.

4 Find the 🏝️ on the map. What surrounds it?

Now you can make your own land and water map. You can draw any kind of land and water you want on the map. Add some animals and houses if you want. Be sure to put everything in the key. Remember to include a title for you map.

_____

Title

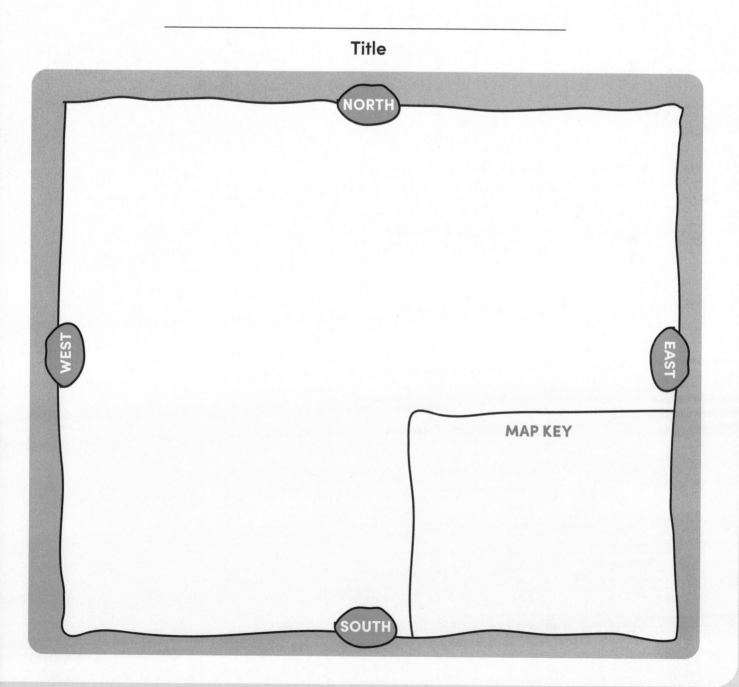

Our World

This map shows our whole world. The large bodies of land are called continents. There are seven continents on Earth.

Earth also has five oceans. You have read that an ocean is a very large body of salty water. Oceans cover most of Earth. Name the five oceans.

. . . .

Use the map to answer the questions.

1 Write the name of Earth's continents.

_____,

_____,

_____,

_____, _____,

_____, _____

2 What is the smallest content? _____

3 What is the largest content? _____

ARCTIC OCEAN

NORTH AMERICA

WEST

PACIFIC OCEAN

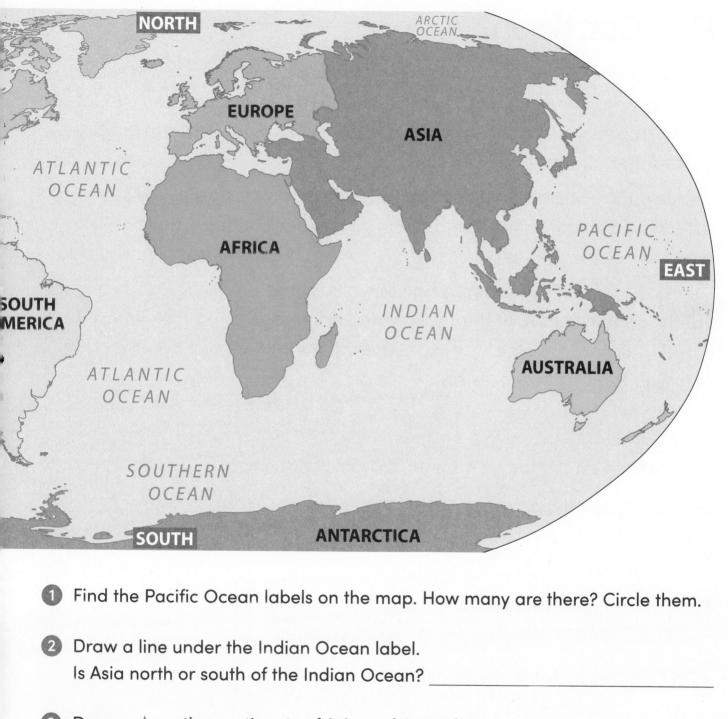

1. Find the Pacific Ocean labels on the map. How many are there? Circle them.

2. Draw a line under the Indian Ocean label.
   Is Asia north or south of the Indian Ocean? _____

3. Draw a ★ on the continents of Asia and Australia.
   Which continent is farther east? _____

4. Draw a ✓ on the continent of Africa.
   Which ocean is west of Africa? _____

Our Continent

The continent we live on is called North America. Our continent has three large countries. A **country** is a land and the people who live there. North America also has some smaller countries. Some countries of North America are islands.

Every country has a national **capital**. The national capital is where the leaders of a country work. Find the symbol for a national capital in the map key on the next page. Draw a circle around that symbol in Canada.

Every country has a border. A **border** tells where one place ends and another begins. Look at the map on the next page. Find the symbol for a national border in the map key. Then draw a ✓ on the boundary between the United States and Canada.

• •

Use the map on the facing page to answer the questions.

1 What country is north of the United States? _____

2 In which direction is Mexico from the United States? _____

3 What ocean is to the east
   of the United States? _____

4 What ocean is to the west
   of the United States? _____

North America

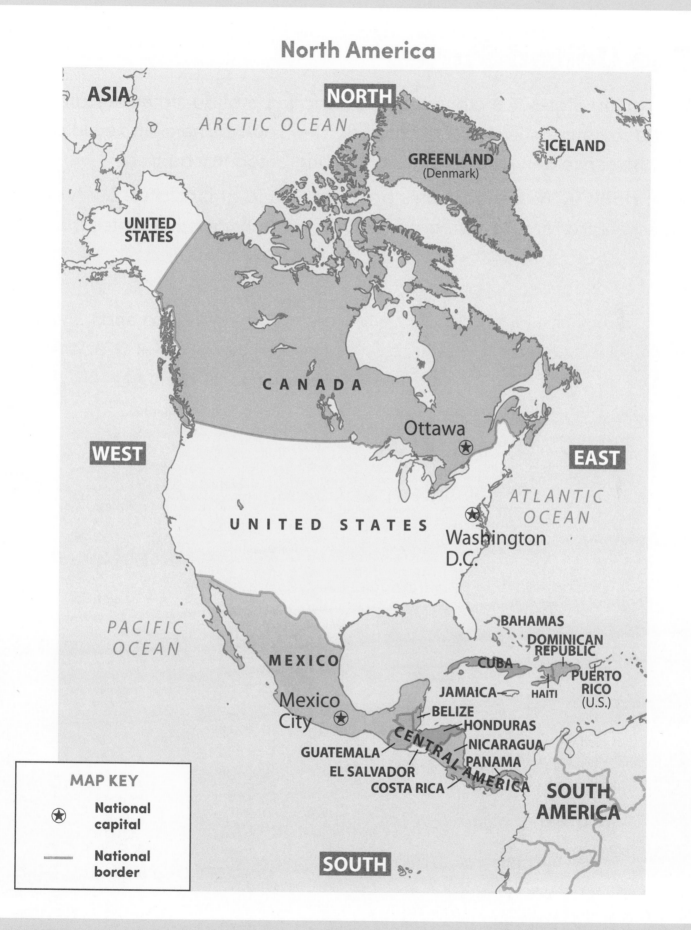

ASIA

ARCTIC OCEAN

NORTH

ICELAND

GREENLAND
(Denmark)

UNITED
STATES

CANADA

Ottawa ⊛

WEST

EAST

ATLANTIC
OCEAN

⊛

UNITED STATES

Washington
D.C.

PACIFIC
OCEAN

MEXICO

BAHAMAS

DOMINICAN
REPUBLIC

CUBA

PUERTO
RICO
(U.S.)

Mexico
City ⊛

JAMAICA

HAITI

BELIZE

HONDURAS

GUATEMALA

CENTRAL AMERICA

NICARAGUA

EL SALVADOR

PANAMA

COSTA RICA

SOUTH
AMERICA

MAP KEY

⊛ National capital

— National border

SOUTH

The United States

The United States is a big country. It is made up of 50 states. A state is part of a country. Every state has a border. Look at the map key to see the difference between a state border and a country border.

Most states in the United States are right next to other states. But two states, Alaska and Hawaii, are far away from all the other states.

The United States

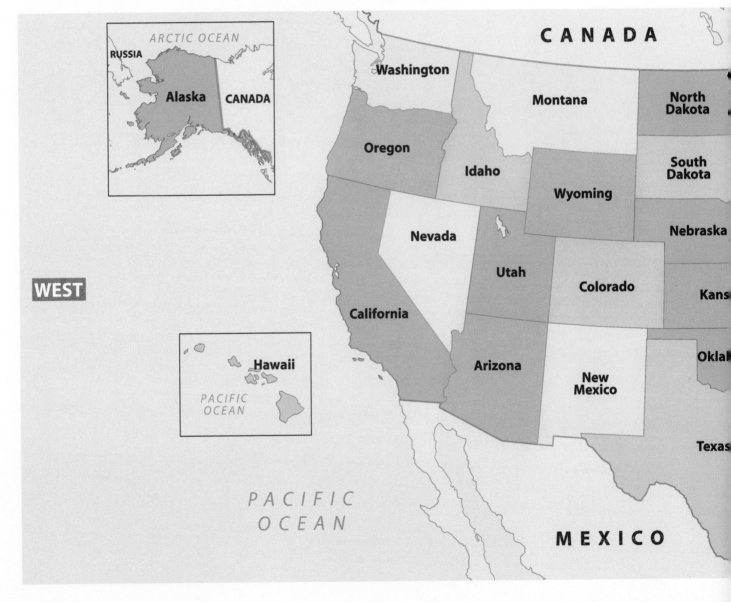

© Scholastic Inc.

Use the map to answer the questions.

① Find Nevada and draw a ✔ on it.

② Draw a ★ on all the states that share a border with Nevada.

③ How many states share a border with Nevada? _____

④ What direction is Utah from Arizona? _____

⑤ To go to Colorado from Kansas you need to go _____.

⑥ Ohio is _____ of Indiana.

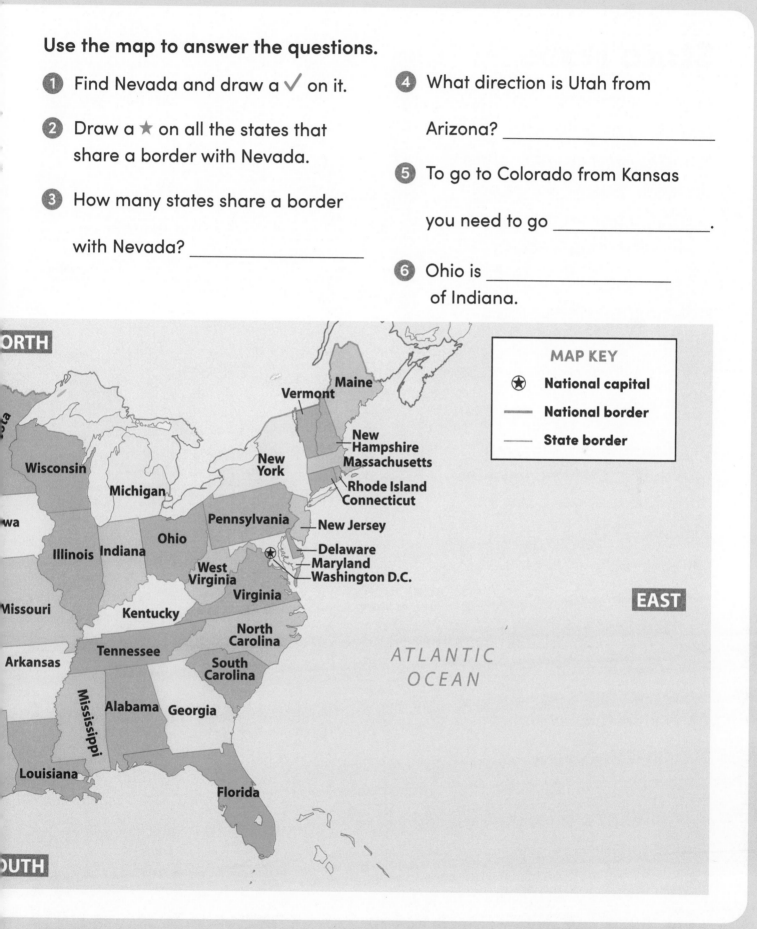

MAP KEY
⊛ National capital
— National border
— State border

NORTH

Maine
Vermont
New Hampshire
New York
Massachusetts
Rhode Island
Connecticut
Wisconsin
Michigan
Pennsylvania
New Jersey
Iowa
Ohio
Delaware
Illinois Indiana
Maryland
West Virginia
Washington D.C.
Missouri
Virginia
Kentucky
North Carolina
EAST
Arkansas
Tennessee
South Carolina
ATLANTIC OCEAN
Mississippi
Alabama Georgia
Louisiana
Florida

SOUTH

State Maps

A state is part of a country. The state of California is one of the largest states in the United States. More people live in California than in any other state in our country.

Rhode Island is the smallest state in the United States. More than 400 Rhode Islands could fit into the state of Alaska!

Use the map of California and the map of Rhode Island on the next page to answer the questions.

1 Look at the map of California. Find the symbol for state capital in the map key. Then, find it on the map and circle it.

2 Look at the map of Rhode Island on page 247. Its state capital is Providence. Draw a ✓ on it.

3 Find the symbol for national border on the California map. Then find it on the map and draw a ★ on it.

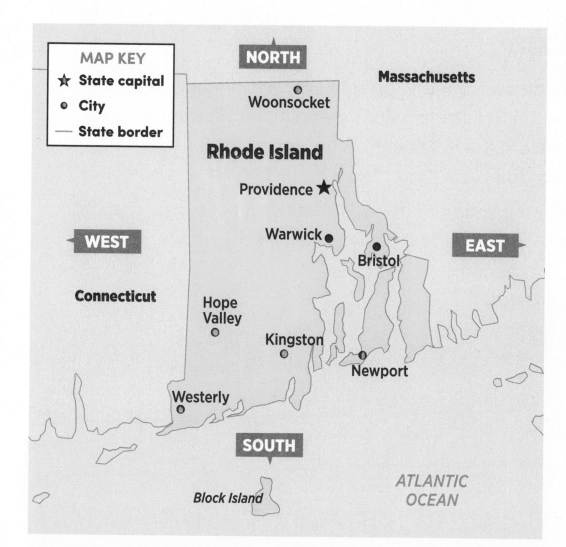

Use the maps to complete each sentence.

1 Mexico is _____ of California.

2 The Pacific Ocean is _____ of California.

3 _____ is to the west of Rhode Island.

4 The Colorado River runs between California and _____.

5 Bristol, Rhode Island, is _____ of Warwick.

A City Map

A city is a big place where many people live. Washington, D.C., is the capital city of the United States. Many people visit Washington, D.C., every year. It is where the President of the United States lives and works. Other leaders live and work there, too.

City maps show the location of major streets and buildings. They can help you go from one place to another when visiting a city.

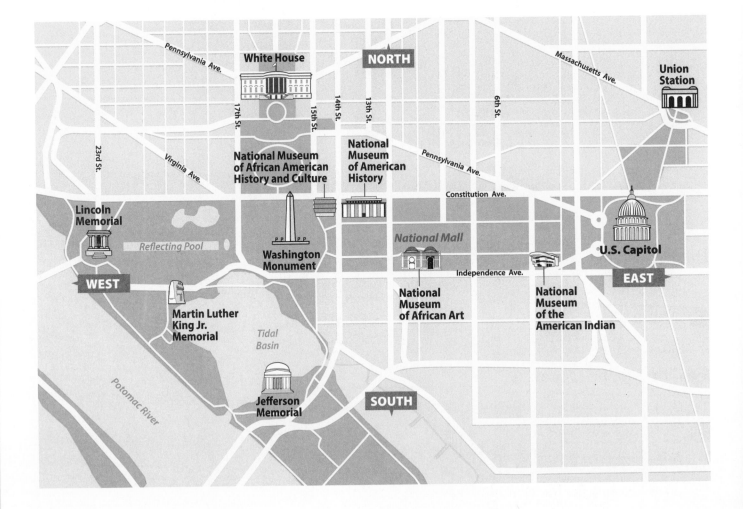

Use the map of Washington, D.C., to answer the questions.

1 Is the Washington Monument north or south of the White House?

_____

2 On what street is the National Museum of African Art?

_____

3 In what direction does Constitution Avenue run? _____

4 What would you like to visit in Washington, D.C.? _____

_____

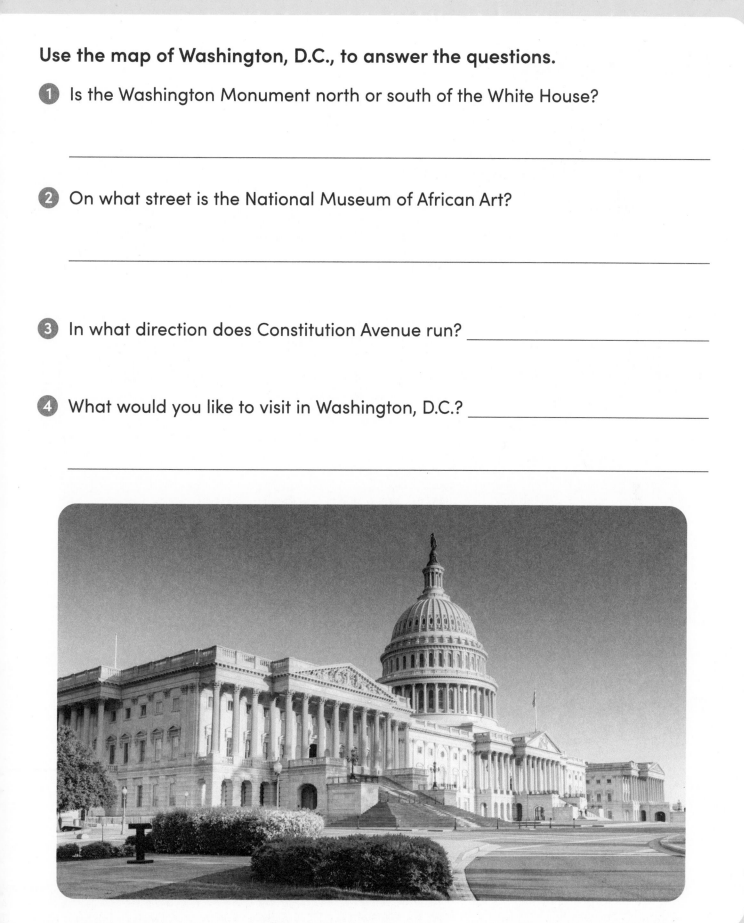

Map Review

Jason's Neighborhood

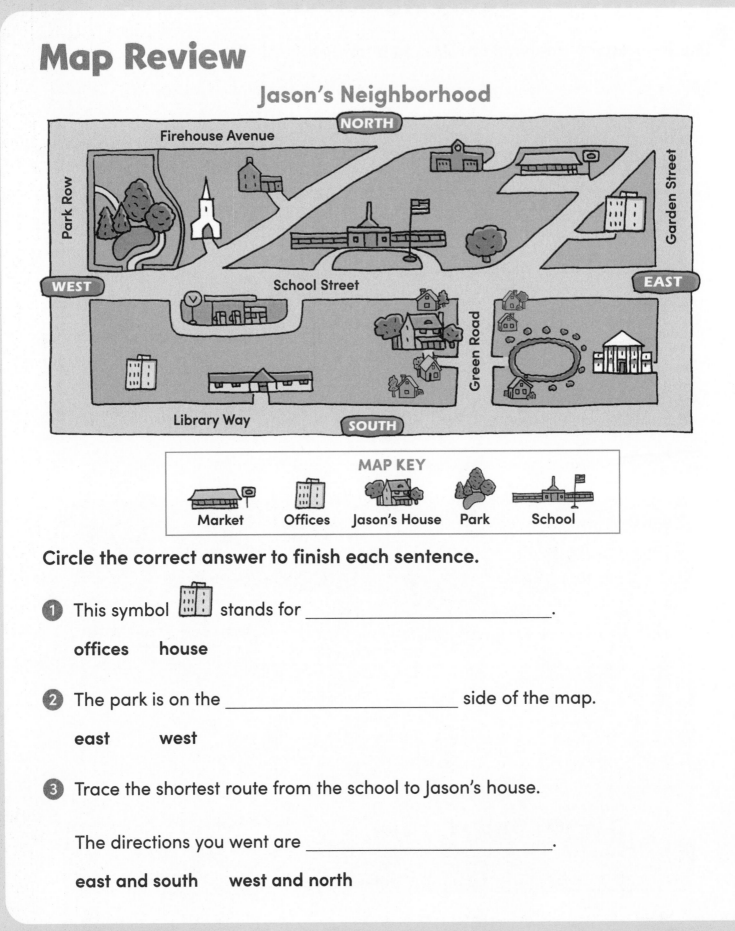

Circle the correct answer to finish each sentence.

1 This symbol ▯ stands for _____.

offices   house

2 The park is on the _____ side of the map.

east   west

3 Trace the shortest route from the school to Jason's house.

The directions you went are _____.

east and south   west and north

The map on this page uses colors to show land.
Underline the sentences that are true about the map.

1 The capital city of North Carolina is Raleigh.

2 North Carolina has mountains, hills, and plains.

3 The Atlantic Ocean to the east of North Carolina.

4 New Bern is north of Raleigh.

North Carolina, Land Features

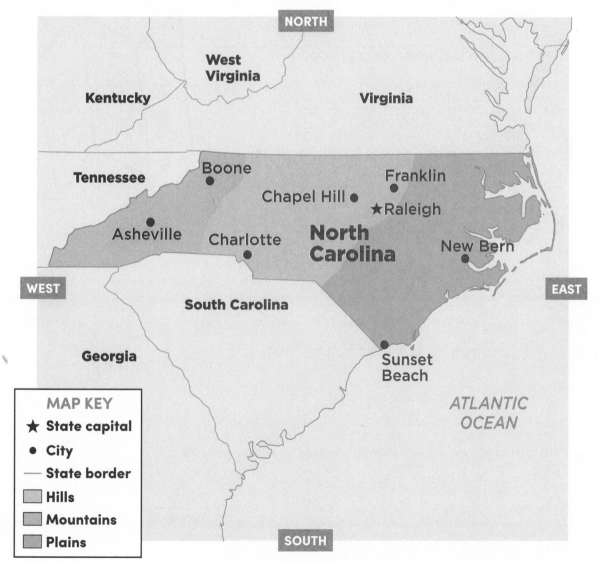

Thinking About Maps

You have learned a lot about maps.
Use what you know to find the secret words.

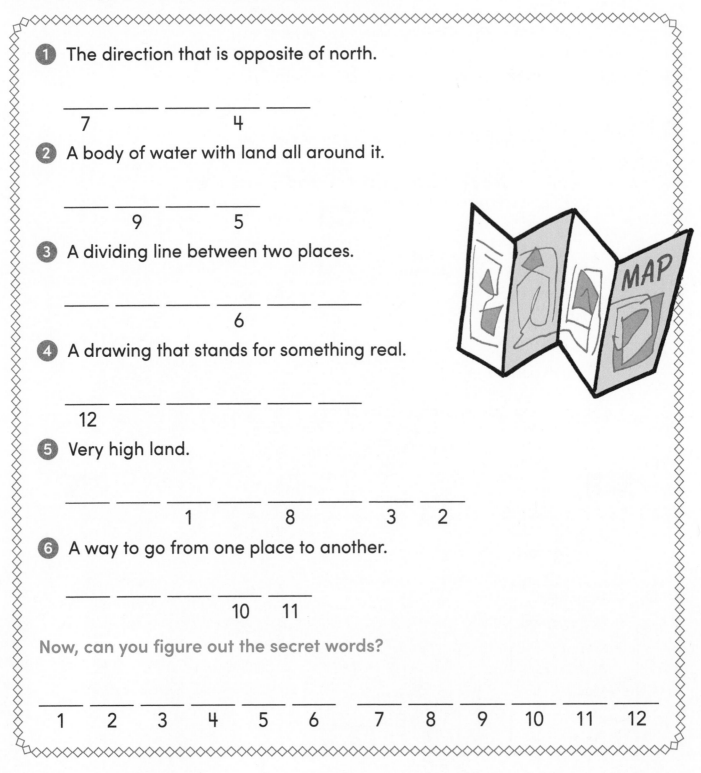

1 The direction that is opposite of north.

___ ___ ___ ___ ___
 7   4

2 A body of water with land all around it.

___ ___ ___ ___
   9   5

3 A dividing line between two places.

___ ___ ___ ___ ___ ___
          6

4 A drawing that stands for something real.

___ ___ ___ ___ ___ ___
 12

5 Very high land.

___ ___ ___ ___ ___ ___ ___
   1   8   3 2

6 A way to go from one place to another.

___ ___ ___ ___ ___
    10 11

Now, can you figure out the secret words?

___ ___ ___ ___ ___ ___ ___ ___ ___ ___ ___ ___
1   2   3   4   5   6   7   8   9 10 11 12

Glossary

border A border is a dividing line between two places.

capital A capital is a city where government leaders work.

continent A continent is a large body of land.
North America is a continent.

country A country is a land where people live.

direction A direction tells where something is.
The four main directions are north, south, east, and west.

east East is one of the four main directions.
East is the opposite of west.

Earth Earth is the planet on which people live.

far *Far* is a word that tells where things are.
Far is the opposite of near.

globe A globe is a model of Earth.

hill A hill is land that is higher than a plain but
not as high as a mountain.

lake A lake is a body of water that has land all around it.

left *Left* is a word that tells where things are.
Left is the opposite of right.

map A map is a drawing of a place from above.
A map shows part or all of Earth.

map key A map key is a list of symbols used on a map.
The map key tells what each symbol means.

Glossary

mountain	A mountain is very high land.
near	*Near* is a word that tells where things are. Near is the opposite of far.
neighborhood	A neighborhood is a place where people live and work.
north	North is one of the four main directions. North is the direction toward the North Pole.
ocean	An ocean is a very large body of water. Earth has five oceans.
plain	A plain is flat land.
right	*Right* is a word that tells where things are. Right is the opposite of left.
river	A river is a body of water that flows across the land.
route	A route is a way to go from one place to another.
south	South is one of the four main directions. South is the direction toward the South Pole.
state	A state is part of the United States. There are 50 states.
symbol	A symbol is a drawing that stands for something real.
west	West is one of the four main directions. West is the opposite of east.

SCIENCE

Beautiful Babies

Cross out every other letter to name the baby animal.
Write the name on the line. The first one has been done for you.

k ~~j~~ i ~~u~~ t ~~g~~ t ~~b~~ e ~~s~~ n

1 <u>Kitten</u>

l v a g m c b

2 _____

t h a t d a p k o r l f e

3 _____

d f u j c w k d l n i k n o g

4 _____

f c a i w d n

5 _____

c e u x b

6 _____

c l a d l n f

7 _____

p d i h g y l i e b t

8 _____

c o h r i e c q k

9 _____

p b u u p a p z y

10 _____

Babies Change and Grow!

Read about animal babies.
Then try the science investigations.

Emperor Penguin

A baby penguin is called a **chick**. Its head is black and white. Its body is covered in fluffy gray feathers called **down**. As the chick grows, its head turns black. It grows new feathers on its body—black for its back and white for its belly.

Silver Leaf Monkey

This baby monkey has bright orange fur. That helps the adults see it in the dark forest. As it grows older, the monkey's fur will change color. It will turn dark gray— just like its parents' fur.

Warty Newt

This is a newt. It lives near a pond. A newt starts out as an egg in the water. When it hatches, it becomes a **larva**. The larva breathes underwater with **gills**, just like a fish. But a newt's gills are on top of its head! When the larva turns into an adult, it lives on land.

larva

adult

Investigation I

An emperor penguin does not leave its egg in a nest. It carries its egg on its feet! What is it like to walk with an egg on your feet? Try it!

Materials

- 1 cup rice
- quart-sized zip-top plastic bag
- sock
- recording sheet (next page)

1. Gather the materials you will need.

2. Pour the rice into the zip-top bag. Press out the air. Seal the bag and roll it up. Put it inside a sock. Tuck in the top of the sock. This is your penguin egg.

3. A penguin father carries his egg on his feet. Put your egg on top of your feet. Carefully walk around the room. If the egg falls off your feet, stop. Pick it up and put it back on your feet.

4. What did you do to make sure the egg stayed on your feet? (Did you turn your feet a new way? Speed up or slow down? What else?) Record on the next page.

5. **Think:** Why do you think penguin fathers carry their eggs on their feet? How do they keep the eggs safe?

1 Do Steps 2 and 3 of the investigation. What happened?

_____

_____

_____

_____

2 What did you do to make sure the egg stayed on your feet?

_____

_____

_____

_____

3 Why do you think penguin fathers carry their eggs on their feet?
How do they keep the eggs safe?

_____

_____

_____

_____

Investigation 2

Some baby animals have bright colors so their parents can find them easily. How can you make a baby bird stand out in its habitat (the nature around it)?

Materials
- crayons
- recording sheet (next page)

1. Gather your materials.

2. Look at the "pretend" habitat below. Look at the picture of the baby birds on the next page. Imagine they will live in that habitat. Will the white birds stand out or blend in?

3. Color Bird 1 so that it will stand out in the habitat.
   Remember: You want your bird to be seen when it's in its habitat.

4. What if you don't want the baby to stand out? What if you want to hide it from enemies? Many baby animals have colors and patterns that make them hard to see. They blend in with their habitats. The name for this kind of blending-in is **camouflage**. Color Bird 2 with camouflage.

1 Look at the pictures of the baby birds below. Imagine they live in the habitat on the previous page. Do the white birds stand out or blend in?

_____

2 Do Step 3 of the investigation. Is your baby bird easy or hard to see?

_____

3 Do Step 4 of the investigation. How did you camouflage (blend in) your baby bird?

_____

Bird 1

Bird 2

All Kinds of Animals

Read each clue. Write the names of the correct animals in the crossword puzzle.

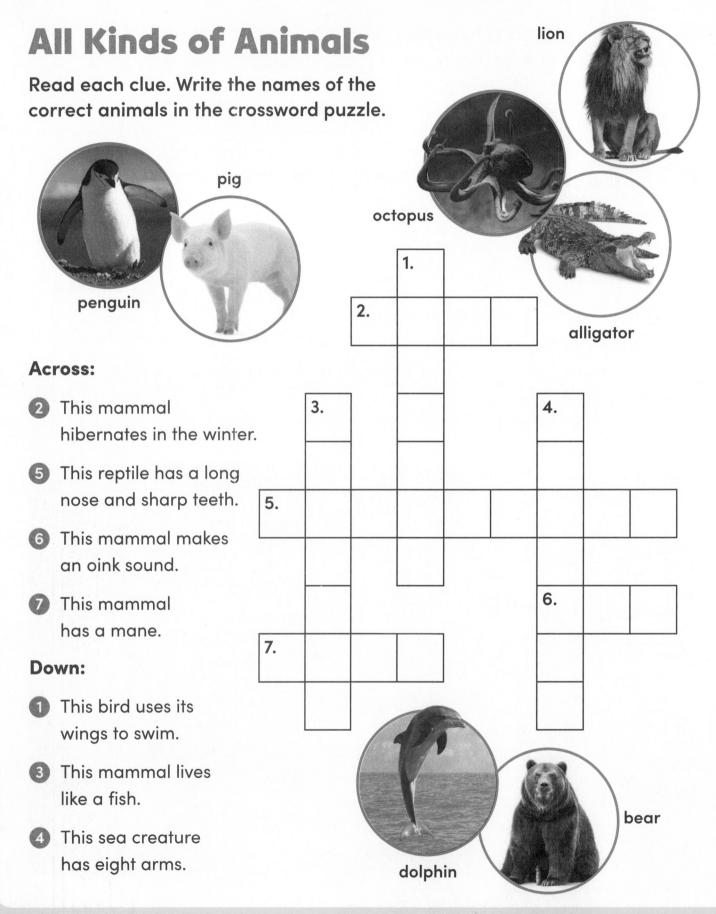

lion

octopus

pig

penguin

alligator

Across:

2 This mammal hibernates in the winter.

5 This reptile has a long nose and sharp teeth.

6 This mammal makes an oink sound.

7 This mammal has a mane.

Down:

1 This bird uses its wings to swim.

3 This mammal lives like a fish.

4 This sea creature has eight arms.

dolphin

bear

A Home for Koalas

Read about koala habitats. Then try the science investigations.

Koalas live in Australia. But people are taking over their habitats, the places where they live. Now there's less food and shelter for the animals.

Koalas are very picky eaters. They eat only the leaves of eucalyptus (yoo-kuh-LIP-tiss) trees. People have cut down many eucalyptus forests. They have turned the land into farms, highways, malls, and houses. Today, there are not many koalas left.

Scientists and other people are now working together to help. They are planting new eucalyptus trees for the koalas. They hope this will help the animals thrive.

Investigation 1

What lives in your community park? Find out!

1. Gather your materials.

2. Close your eyes and imagine you are walking around your community park. What different ways do people use it? Record your thoughts on the next page.

3. What other living things do you think might use your community park? They might be living there, or they might just visit. Make a list.

4. Go on a Community Park Safari. Look for signs of life. You can look for living things, like a tree or a butterfly. (Don't touch or disturb anything!) You can also look for clues that something was there. Maybe you will see a nibbled leaf, a spider web, or an animal track. Look carefully at what you find.

5. On your recording sheet, draw two things you found.

6. Share your discoveries with a friend. What surprised you the most?

  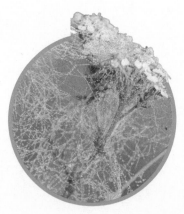

1 What different ways do people use your community park?

_____

_____

2 What other living things do you think might use your community park?

_____

_____

3 What signs of life did you find on your Community Park Safari?
Draw two things you found.

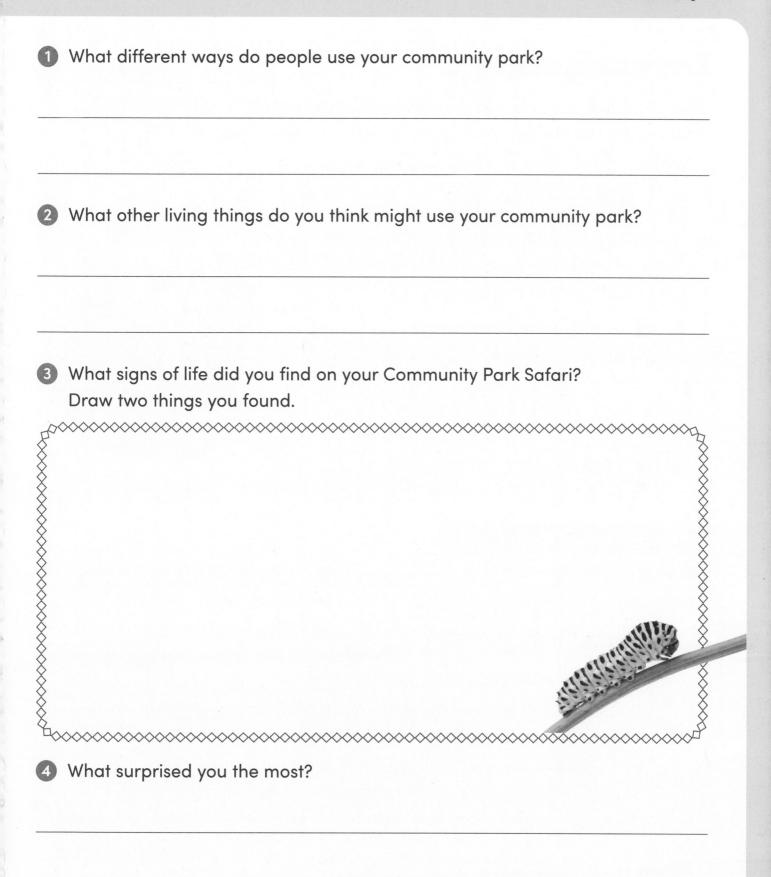

4 What surprised you the most?

_____

_____

Investigation 2

**What would you like to live in your community park?
How would you change your park to make it a good home?**

Materials

- pencil
- recording sheet (next page)

1. List three animals or plants you would like to have in your community park.

2. Look at your list. Does your community park have what each one needs to survive? (For clues, use the chart below.)

3. Pick one living thing that could not get what it needs from your community park. How could you change your community park so it would be a good habitat for your plant or animal? Write your ideas on your recording sheet. Draw a picture of the changes.

What Do Living Things Need?

Each kind of living thing has its own special needs. Here are some to think about.	
Food	Some animals eat plants. Some eat other animals.
Water	Some animals just need water to drink. Some plants need to soak up water with their roots. But other plants and animals live in the water, so they need a lot more.
Shelter	An animal might need a cave or a good place to dig an underground burrow. It might need a branch and twigs for making a nest.
Territory	Some animals never travel very far. Some hunt over large areas. Others fly or swim thousands of miles every year.
Temperature	Some plants and animals need warmth. Some are happy in the cold.
Amount of Light	Some plants need a lot of sun. Some grow well in the shade.

1 List three animals or plants you would like to have in your community park.

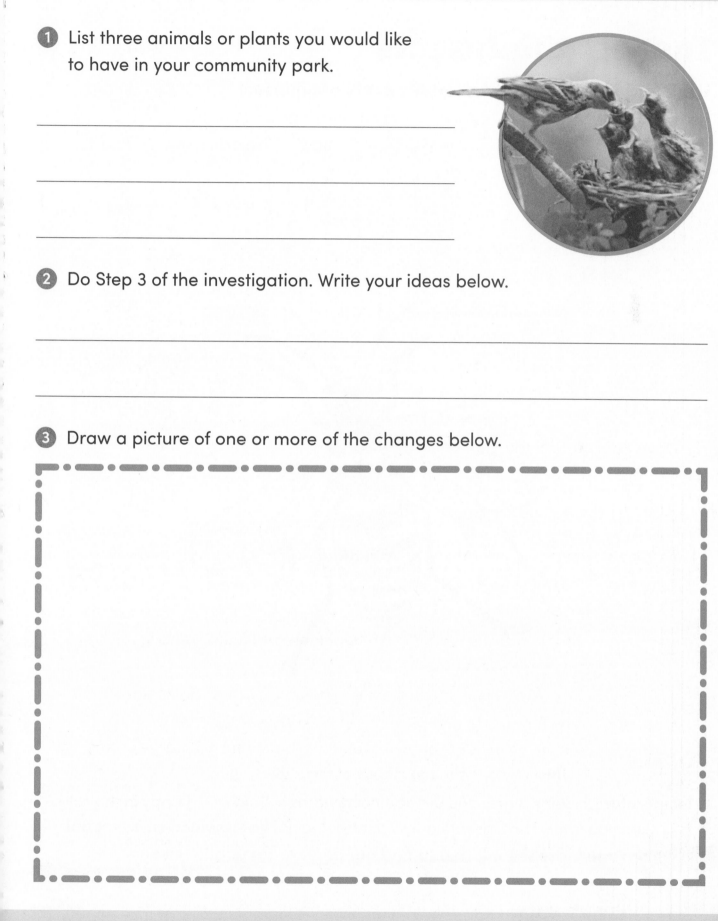

_____

_____

_____

2 Do Step 3 of the investigation. Write your ideas below.

_____

_____

3 Draw a picture of one or more of the changes below.

Inspect the Insects

Use the words in the box to identify parts of an insect.

leg	antenna	wing	head	abdomen	thorax

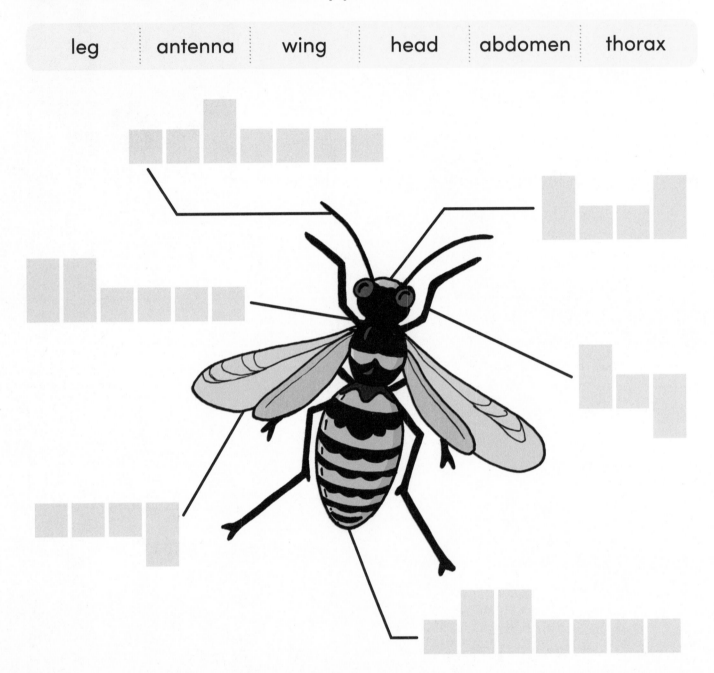

⭐ Did you know that insects only have six legs? That is why a spider is not an insect. Use the internet to find out another fact about insects.

Way to 'Bee' Helpful!

Read about bees. Then try the science investigations.

1. A honeybee visits a flower to drink its nectar. Later, the bee will use the nectar to make honey.

2. The bee also gathers tiny grains called pollen. It takes the pollen back to the hive for food. Some extra pollen sticks to the bee's body.

3. The bee flies to a new flower.

4. Some of the extra pollen rubs off of the bee's body. The pollen sticks to the new flower.

5. The pollen goes into the flower. It helps form seeds. A fruit grows around the seeds. Someday a hungry animal might eat the fruit. The seeds might drop to the ground and grow into new plants!

Investigation 1

How do bees pollinate flowers? Find out here!

Materials

- 4 tsps glitter (different colors)
- 4 small paper cups
- yellow and black pipe-cleaners
- pencil
- recording sheet (next page)

1. Gather the materials you will need.

2. Make a paper-cup flower: Put 1 teaspoon of colored glitter in a small paper cup. The glitter is the flower's pollen. Make 3 more flowers. Use different colors of glitter.

3. Make a pipe-cleaner bee as shown in the diagram below: Wrap a yellow then a black pipe-cleaner around a pencil.

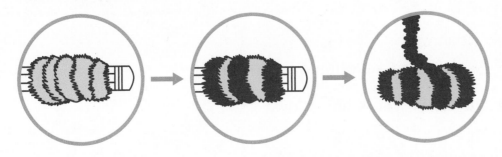

4. Fly your bee into a flower. Gently tap your bee around the bottom of the flower. Your bee is drinking nectar and gathering pollen.

5. Fly your bee into a new flower. Choose one with a different color of glitter. Gently tap your bee around the bottom of that flower.

6. Fly your bee to two more flowers. Make sure you visit a flower with every color of glitter.

7. Return to the first flower. Look inside. Do you see pollen from other flowers? (Look for glitter of other colors.) If so, your flower was pollinated!

8. **Think:** The job of flowers is to attract pollinators. Why is that job important? Why are bees important to flowers? Why are flowers important to bees?

1 Do Steps 2—7 of the investigation. Do you see "pollen" from other flowers?

_____

2 **Think:** Why is it important for flowers to attract pollinators?

_____

_____

_____

3 Why are bees important to flowers?

_____

_____

_____

4 Why are flowers important to bees?

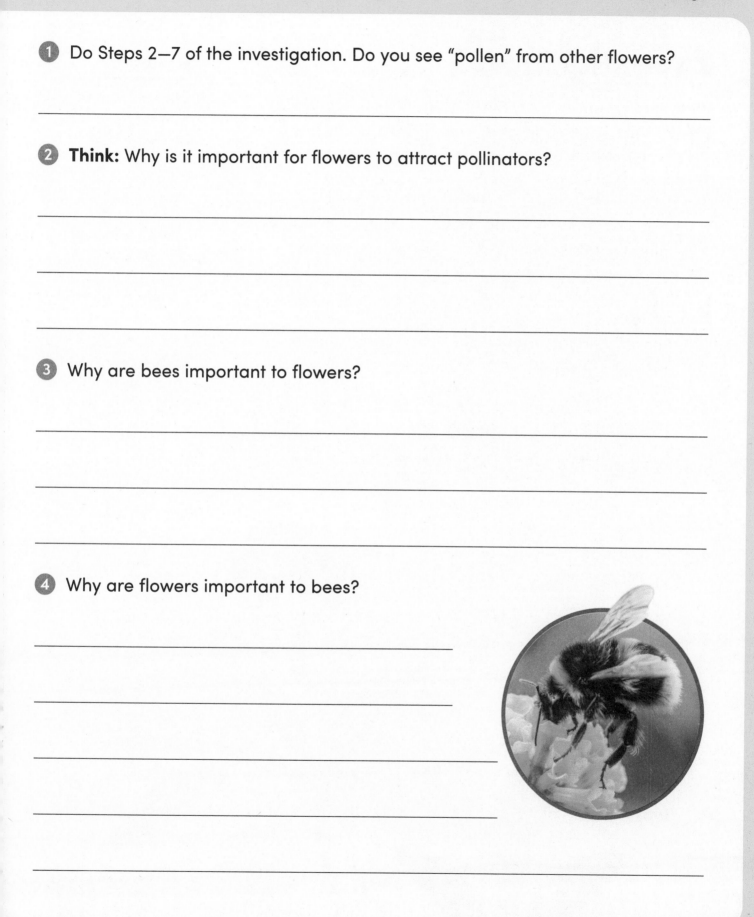

_____

_____

_____

_____

Investigation 2

Different animals help move pollen from flower to flower. But each animal likes a different kind of flower. Design a flower to attract a pollinator.

1. Look at the four pollinators on the next page. Choose a pollinator and design a flower for that animal. Look at the list of things it likes. Draw a flower for your pollinator on the next page.

2. Gather materials and make a flower for your pollinator. Think about color. Think about shape. Think about smell.

3. Pick a different pollinator. Find a flower that it would like. Draw it on a separate sheet of paper. Write about which pollinator you think would like it and why.

Materials

- things to make a flower (colored paper, markers, crayons, scissors, tape)
- a sweet-smelling liquid, like vanilla extract (optional)
- a fruity-smelling liquid, like lemon extract (optional)
- crayons or markers
- recording sheet (next page)

What Pollinators Like

Bee	Butterfly	Beetle	Hummingbird
• a place it can land (like a petal) • yellow or blue color • sweet smell	• a place it can land (like a petal) • tiny tubes for butterfly tongues to gather nectar • pink or light purple color • sweet smell	• large flower • flat or dish-shaped flower (easy for beetle to climb on) • green or white color • spicy or fruity smell	• long tube shape (big enough for the bird's head and beak) • red or orange color • no smell needed

1. Do Step 1 of the investigation. Draw a flower for your pollinator.

2. Now do Step 3 of the investigation. Draw a flower for a different pollinator on a separate sheet of paper. Write about which pollinator you think would like it and why.

Which Insect Is It?

Read the article about insects. Then follow the directions in the box.

Is it a **butterfly**? Or is it a **moth**?

Both kinds of insects are colorful. Most butterflies have bright colors. Moths have pale colors.

Butterflies and moths need to keep warm. But they keep warm in different ways. A butterfly warms itself in the sun. A moth warms up by moving its wings.

Both insects fly. Butterflies fly in the day. But moths fly at night.

Butterfly

Moth

© Scholastic Inc.

Answer each question. Use the article and photos.

1 This article compares and contrasts _____.

○ day and night

○ moths and butterflies

○ flying and resting

What helped you answer?

_____

_____

2 What does a moth do to stay warm?

○ It rests in the sun.

○ It flaps its wings.

○ It sleeps under its wings.

What helped you answer?

_____

_____

3 What is another way that butterflies and moths are different?

_____

_____

_____

Auks and Hawks

Read the article about birds. Then follow the directions in the box.

Auks and **hawks** are birds.

Like all birds, both lay eggs. Both fly and hunt.

In other ways, auks and hawks are different. Auks are black and white. Hawks come in many colors.

Auks have short legs with webbed feet. Hawks have long, strong legs. They have sharp claws.

Auks eat fish and other sea life. Hawks eat small land animals, snakes, and insects.

Text Marking

Compare and contrast auks and hawks.

☐ Draw boxes around the signal words **both, but,** and **different**.

◯ Circle one way they are alike.

＿ <u>Underline</u> one way they are different.

Auk

Hawk

Answer each question. Use the article and photos.

1 This article compares and contrasts _____.

   ○ claws and webbed feet

   ○ birds and fish

   ○ hawks and auks

What helped you answer?

_____

_____

2 What is a way that auks and hawks are ALIKE?

   ○ Both eat snakes.

   ○ Both lay eggs.

   ○ Both have long legs.

What helped you answer?

_____

_____

3 Look at the photos. Which is the hawk? Which is the auk? Write how you can tell.

_____

_____

_____

Name That Dinosaur

Write the dinosaur name that goes with each clue.

I am one of the longest dinosaurs.

__ __ __ __ __ __ __ __ __ __ __ __ __ __
        6   4

I am the fiercest dinosaur.

__ __ __ __ __ __ __ __ __ __ __ __ __ __ __ __ __
3   2

I am a spike-tailed dinosaur.

__ __ __ __ __ __ __ __ __ __
    7

I am a three-horned dinosaur.

__ __ __ __ __ __ __ __ __ __
          1

I am a duck-billed dinosaur.

__ __ __ __ __ __ __ __ __
                 5

Use the letters above to finish the rhyme.

Dinosaurs were amazing creatures, I think
But I'll never see a real one because they are...

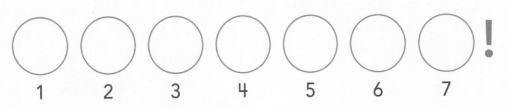

1   2   3   4   5   6   7

Trachodon

Brachiosaurus

Tyrannosaurus Rex

Triceratops

Stegosaurus

Plants We Eat

Read the paragraph. Then answer the questions.

We eat many foods that come from plants. Do you eat apples and bananas? They are fruits. Do you eat toast or cereal? They are made from grains like wheat, oats, and rice. How about carrots, celery, and potatoes? They are vegetables. Fruits, grains, and vegetables all come from plants.

1 The main idea of this paragraph is

○ cereal is made from grains.

○ carrots are vegetables.

○ many foods we eat come from plants.

2 Apples are

○ vegetables.

○ fruits.

○ grains.

3 If you eat a banana on cereal, you eat

○ fruit and grains.

○ two vegetables.

○ plants and animals.

Thumbs Up!

**Read the article about the human body.
Then follow the directions in the box.**

Thumbs are special fingers. All your fingers can move in and out. All can move from side to side. All can bend and wiggle. All can move in a circle. But only a thumb can touch every other fingertip. No other fingers can meet like this. Try it. Your thumbs help you grab and hold things. Can you pick up a penny without using your thumb?

Answer each question. Use the article and photos.

1 What is something ONLY thumbs can do?

○ bend and wiggle
○ move in a circle
○ touch every other fingertip

What helped you answer?

_____

_____

2 What do your thumbs help you do?

○ wiggle
○ pick things up
○ count pennies

What helped you answer?

_____

_____

3 Try to pick up a penny without using your thumb. What happens? Write about it.

_____

_____

_____

Ahhh...choo!

Read the health article. Then follow the directions in the box.

Almost anything can cause a sneeze. You might breathe in some dust, cold air, or even pepper. It tickles the inside of your nose. So you need to clear it out.

Your brain gets the message. It signals some muscles to get ready to help. When they do, you suddenly feel the results. Your eyes close tight. Your mouth opens, and you sneeze: AHHH. . .CHOO! The tickle is gone.

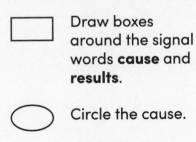

Text Marking

Find the cause and effects.

Draw boxes around the signal words **cause** and **results**.

Circle the cause.

Underline the effects.

Answer each question. Use the article and photos.

1 What does your brain do when your nose feels a tickle inside?

○ It sends messages to muscles that can help.

○ It removes dust from your nose.

○ It makes you feel sleepy.

What helped you answer?

_____

_____

2 Which is NOT an effect of having a tickle inside your nose?

○ You sneeze.

○ Your mouth opens.

○ You feel ticklish all over.

What helped you answer?

_____

_____

3 How does sneezing make you feel better?

_____

_____

_____

The Four Seasons

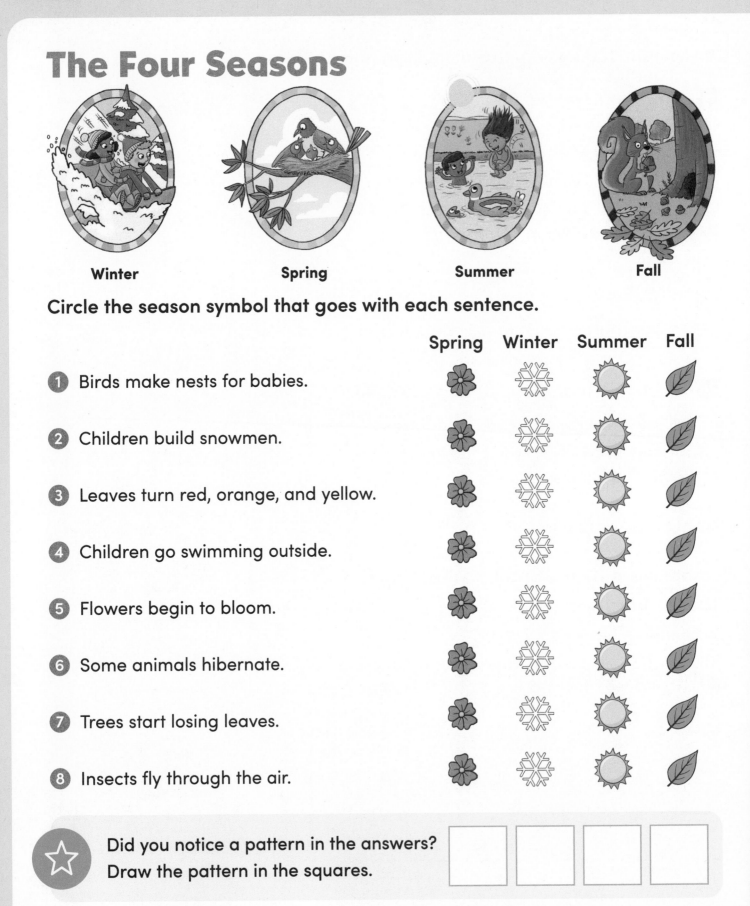

Winter **Spring** **Summer** **Fall**

Circle the season symbol that goes with each sentence.

	Spring	Winter	Summer	Fall
1 Birds make nests for babies.				
2 Children build snowmen.				
3 Leaves turn red, orange, and yellow.				
4 Children go swimming outside.				
5 Flowers begin to bloom.				
6 Some animals hibernate.				
7 Trees start losing leaves.				
8 Insects fly through the air.				

⭐ Did you notice a pattern in the answers?
Draw the pattern in the squares.

The Changing Seasons

Read about the four seasons. Then try the science investigations.

Spring! The sun stays out a long time. The air gets warmer. What a nice change from the cold, dark winter. Plants start to bloom. Insects come out. So do animals that count on them for food.

In the summer, the weather gets hotter. There's still plenty of food. But little by little, the sun rises later and sets earlier.

In autumn the air gets cooler. Leaves change colors. They fall off trees. Some animals gather as much food as they can. Others travel to warmer places.

The days are short and cold. **Winter** has come! Most plants and trees are bare. There's hardly any food to eat. Animals take shelter to keep warm. Others **hibernate**, or go into deep sleep. Maybe they're dreaming of spring!

Investigation I

Keep track of how long or short the days are. Is it spring, summer, fall, or winter? Your calendar may tell you. But you can also find your own clues to the season.

Materials

- clipboard
- pencil
- recording sheet (next page)

1. Gather your materials.

2. Write the current season on the next page. (If you need to, ask an adult for help.)

3. **Think:** What would you expect the weather to be like during this season? What would plants look like? What would animals be doing? What would people be wearing or doing? Write or draw your answers on your recording sheet.

4. Now go outside. Look for clues about each item on your list. Write or draw what you found on your recording sheet.

5. Pick one other season. What do you think would be different if you looked for clues in that season?

Current Season: _____

	What I expect...	Clue I found...
Weather		
Plants		
Animals		
People		

Pick a different season. What do you think would
be different if you looked for clues in that season?
Write your answer on a separate sheet of paper.

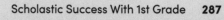

Investigation 2

Keep track of how long or short the days are.

1. Look at the Season Tracker. How many seasons do you see? How many months do you see?

2. Find the current month. What season is it? (**Hint:** Look to the right of the month.) Are the days getting longer or shorter? During which seasons are the days getting longer? During which seasons are the days getting shorter?

3. The length of a day is the time between sunrise and sunset. Look up the times of today's sunrise and sunset. Write the times in the chart on the next page.

4. **Predict:** In one week, what will be the times for sunrise and sunset? Record your guesses.

5. Wait one week. Find the actual times for sunrise and sunset. Record your results.

6. Do Steps 4 and 5 again for the following week. Look at your chart. What do you notice?

Materials
- pencil
- recording sheet (next page)

Season Tracker

Month	Season
January	**Winter** Days are getting longer.
February	
March	**Spring Equinox** Day and night are equal.
April	**Spring** Days are getting longer.
May	
June	**Summer Solstice** Longest day and shortest night
July	**Summer** Days are getting shorter.
August	
September	**Fall Equinox** Day and night are equal.
October	**Fall** Days are getting shorter.
November	
December	**Winter Solstice** Shortest day and longest night

1 What season is it? _____

2 Are the days getting longer or shorter? _____

3 During which seasons are the days getting longer?

_____

4 During which seasons are the days getting shorter?

_____

5 Record the times for sunrise and sunset in the chart below.

	Sunrise time	Sunset time
Today's date: _____		
Date (one week later): _____	I predict:_____ Actual time:_____	I predict:_____ Actual time:_____
Date (two weeks later): _____	I predict:_____ Actual time:_____	I predict:_____ Actual time:_____

High Waters

Read the article. Then follow the directions in the box.

A **flood** happens when water spills over.

What causes a flood? Snow melts off

mountains in the spring. It turns into water.

The water runs downhill. It flows into rivers.

Rainstorms add more water to rivers.

Rivers can't hold all that extra water. So they

overflow. The water covers everything

nearby. Floods soak fields, roads, and towns.

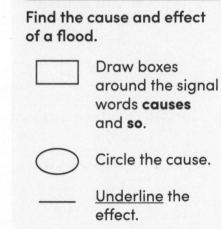

Text Marking

Find the cause and effect of a flood.

▭	Draw boxes around the signal words **causes** and **so**.
◯	Circle the cause.
___	<u>Underline</u> the effect.

A flooded home

Answer each question. Use the article and photos.

1 The word overflow means _____.

○ heat up   ○ spill over   ○ get cold

What helped you answer?

_____

_____

2 Which does NOT cause floods?

○ rain   ○ melting snow   ○ fields and towns

What helped you answer?

_____

_____

3 Why do you think most floods happen in spring?

_____

_____

_____

Weather Watchers

Look at the weather pictures. Read the weather clues. Cross out every other letter. The letters that are left will name the kind of weather. Write the weather word on the line. The first one has been done for you.

I see nothing but snow.

| b | ~~e~~ | l | ~~n~~ | i | ~~s~~ | z | ~~a~~ | z | ~~l~~ | a | ~~o~~ | r | ~~f~~ | d |

1 _blizzard_

I see balls of ice falling from the sky.

| h | j | a | j | i | i | l |

2 _____

I see a dark funnel cloud in the sky.

| t | r | o | p | r | b | n | g | a | j | d | u | o |

3 _____

I see water drops falling from the sky.

| r | g | a | k | i | a | n |

4 _____

I see white flakes falling from the sky.

| s | e | n | b | o | i | w |

5 _____

I see beautiful blue skies.

| s | f | u | s | n | c | s | l | h | o | i | r | n | r | e |

6 _____

Powerful Push

Read about wind. Then try the science investigations.

Wind is moving air. Its force can blow your hat off your head. It can turn your umbrella inside out. Very strong storm winds can even blow the roof off a house.

We can't control the wind. But people have learned how to use the wind's power. We can use it to sail boats. We can use it to keep kites high in the air. We can even use it to make electricity for our homes. How else can we use wind?

Investigation I

Use wind power to give this toy a push!

Materials

- sheet of paper
- pencil
- ruler
- scissors
- recording sheet (next page)

1. Gather the materials you will need.

2. Look at the square below. Use it as a guide to make your own spin wheel. Follow these steps:
    - Use a ruler to draw a square that measures 4 inches tall by 4 inches wide on a separate sheet of paper.
    - Copy the shapes and dashed lines onto your own square.
    - Cut out the square.

3. With the printed side up, fold it in half so the bottom edge meets the top edge. Unfold.

4. Fold it in half again so the right edge meets the left edge. Unfold.

5. Flip the paper over so the blank side is up. Fold one corner to its opposite corner. Unfold.

6. Fold so that the other two corners meet. Unfold.

7. Flip the paper over. Gently push on all four circles. The middle of the paper should poke up in a point.

8. Hold a pencil with the tip pointing up. Balance the folded paper on the tip.

9. You can blow air at the Spin Wheel to give it a push. **Predict:** Which parts of the Spin Wheel could you push (or blow) to make it spin?

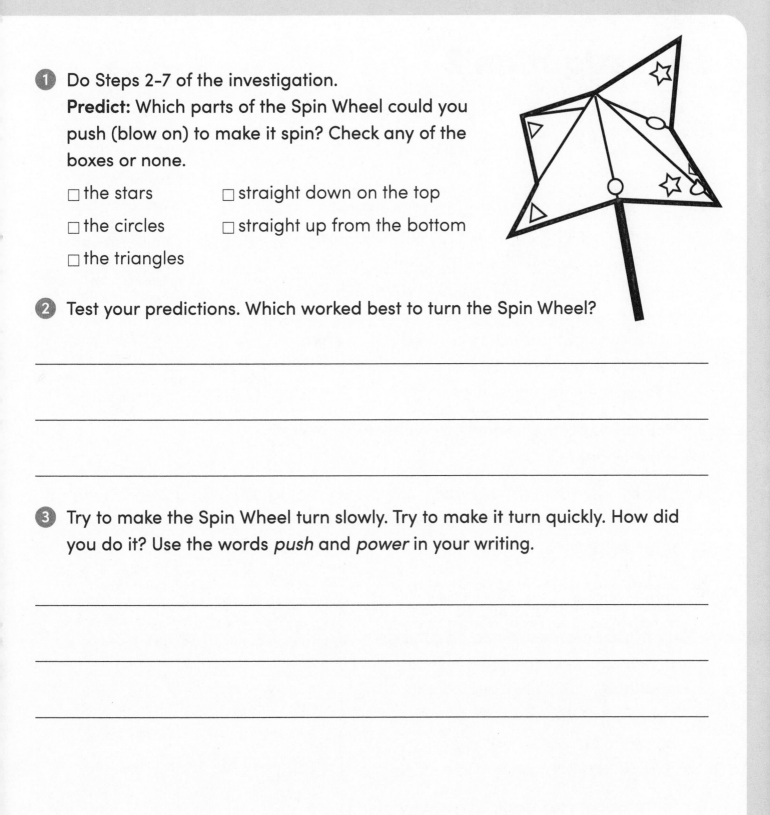

1 Do Steps 2-7 of the investigation.

Predict: Which parts of the Spin Wheel could you push (blow on) to make it spin? Check any of the boxes or none.

☐ the stars   ☐ straight down on the top

☐ the circles   ☐ straight up from the bottom

☐ the triangles

2 Test your predictions. Which worked best to turn the Spin Wheel?

_____

_____

_____

3 Try to make the Spin Wheel turn slowly. Try to make it turn quickly. How did you do it? Use the words *push* and *power* in your writing.

_____

_____

_____

Investigation 2

**What would help your toy catch the wind better?
Try this!**

Materials

- tracing paper
- ruler
- pencil
- scissors
- tape
- inventor's materials: paper, index cards, straws, pipe cleaners, egg cartons, plastic wrap, store-bought feathers
- recording sheet (next page)

1. Gather the materials you will need.

2. Follow these steps to make a Super Spinner:
    - Trace the circle below onto a separate sheet of paper. Copy all lines and shading.
    - Cut out the circle. Then cut along the dotted lines.
    - Line up the cut edge with the solid line. The gray pattern will be covered up. The two halves of the star will line up.
    - Tape down the edges.

3. Put your cone over a pencil point. Blow on it gently. What happens?

4. **Think:** How could you change your cone to make it spin like a Spin Wheel? (**Hint:** You can cut and fold it. You can tape new pieces on to it.) Write down three ideas that might work.

5. Pick one of your ideas and test it. (**Hint:** It's important to keep your changes balanced. If you add things to only one side, the cone will fall off the pencil!) If your idea works, think of ways to make it even better. If it doesn't work, pick a different idea to test.

6. Write about your best design. Why can it spin when you blow on it? Did you run into any problems? How did you fix them?

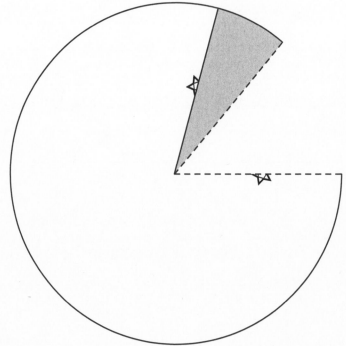

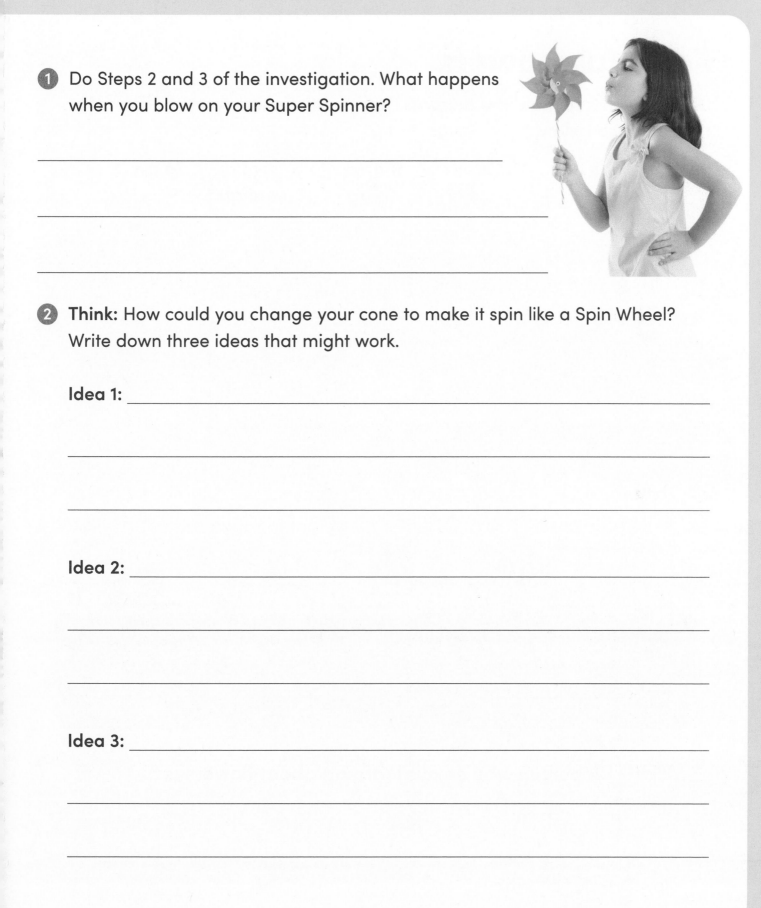

1 Do Steps 2 and 3 of the investigation. What happens when you blow on your Super Spinner?

_____

_____

_____

2 **Think:** How could you change your cone to make it spin like a Spin Wheel? Write down three ideas that might work.

Idea 1: _____

_____

_____

Idea 2: _____

_____

_____

Idea 3: _____

_____

_____

Fanciful Flowers

Use the words to label the picture. Then use the shape code to complete the sentence below.

⬡s⬡eed   stem   fl⬡o⬡wer   rai⬡n⬡   le⬡a⬡f
roo⬡t⬡s   so⬡i⬡l   ⬡b⬡ug   sunligh⬡t⬡

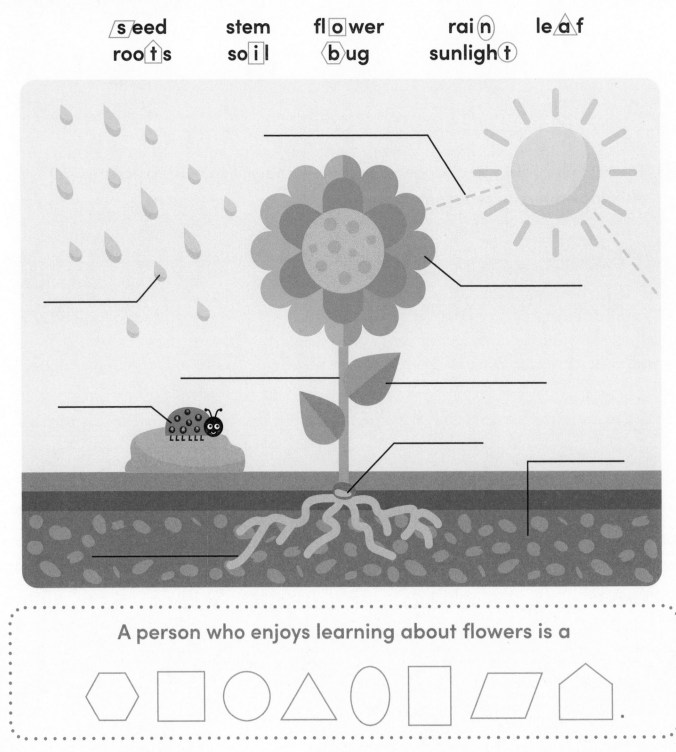

A person who enjoys learning about flowers is a

⬡ ▢ ◯ △ ⬭ ▢ ▱ ⌂ .

Out of This World

Use the grid to identify each planet.

3	Neptune	Earth	Mars
2	Uranus	Saturn	Venus
1	Mercury	Jupiter	
	A	**B**	**C**

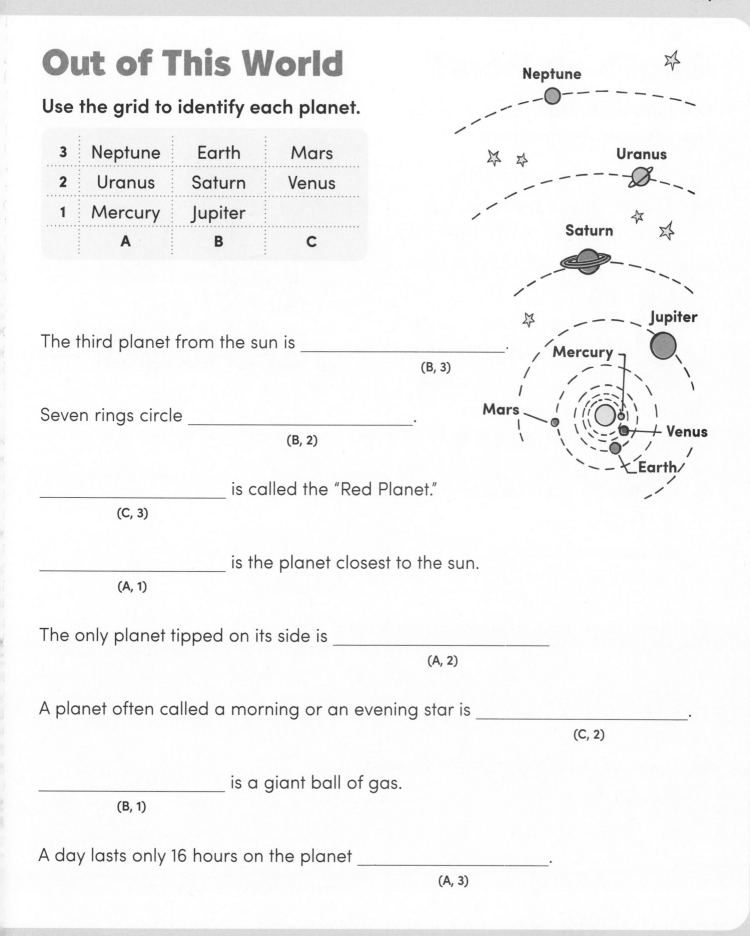

The third planet from the sun is _____.
(B, 3)

Seven rings circle _____.
(B, 2)

_____ is called the "Red Planet."
(C, 3)

_____ is the planet closest to the sun.
(A, 1)

The only planet tipped on its side is _____
(A, 2)

A planet often called a morning or an evening star is _____.
(C, 2)

_____ is a giant ball of gas.
(B, 1)

A day lasts only 16 hours on the planet _____.
(A, 3)

What's on Mars?

Read the paragraph.
Then answer the questions.

The planet Mars is called the
Red Planet. That's because it is
covered in reddish dust. How did
scientists learn what Mars is like?
They sent a robot to Mars.
The robot collected rocks and dirt.
It also took pictures and sent them
back to Earth. Scientists studied
the rocks, dirt, and pictures.
They learned that Mars is cold and dry.

1 What did the robot do after it took pictures?

○ It collected rocks.
○ It sent them to Earth.
○ It landed on Mars.

2 The pictures must have shown that Mars is

○ hot.
○ wet.
○ red.

3 The word *dry* in this paragraph means

○ dirty.
○ not wet.
○ rocky.

SCHOLASTIC SUCCESS WITH

MATH

Funny Dog

Add. Color the picture using the Color Key.

Color Key

1	white
2	orange
3	black
4	tan
5	purple
6	green
7	blue
8	brown
9	yellow
10	red

Lovey Ladybugs

Write a number sentence to show how many spots each ladybug has.

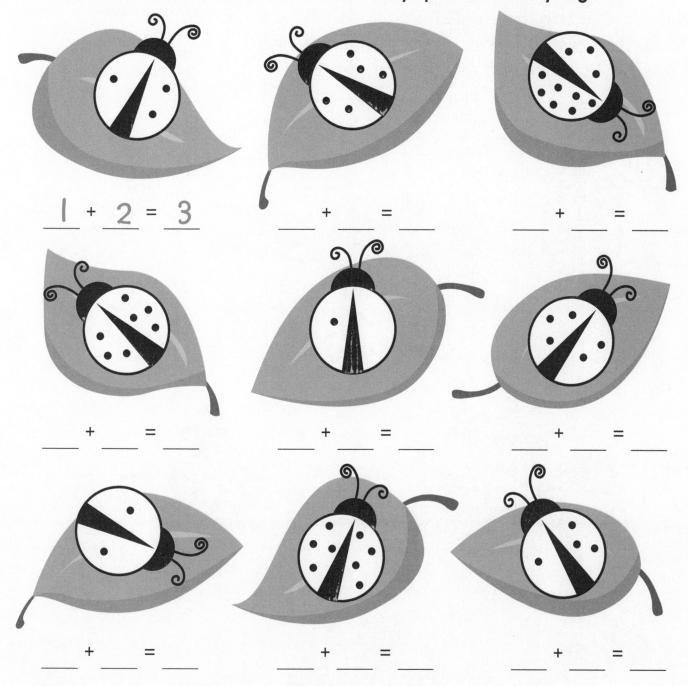

___1___ + ___2___ = ___3___

___ + ___ = ___

___ + ___ = ___

___ + ___ = ___

___ + ___ = ___

___ + ___ = ___

___ + ___ = ___

___ + ___ = ___

___ + ___ = ___

⭐ Color the ladybug with the greatest number of spots red.
Color the ladybug with the least number of spots blue.

Beautiful Bouquets

Look at the number on each bow. Draw more
flowers to match the number written on the bow.
Then, color the bows with an even number yellow.
Color the bows with an odd number purple.

An **even number**
can be divided
evenly into two
whole numbers.
An **odd number**
cannot be divided
evenly into 2 whole
numbers.

Snowflake Math

Add. Color the picture.
Use the color key below.

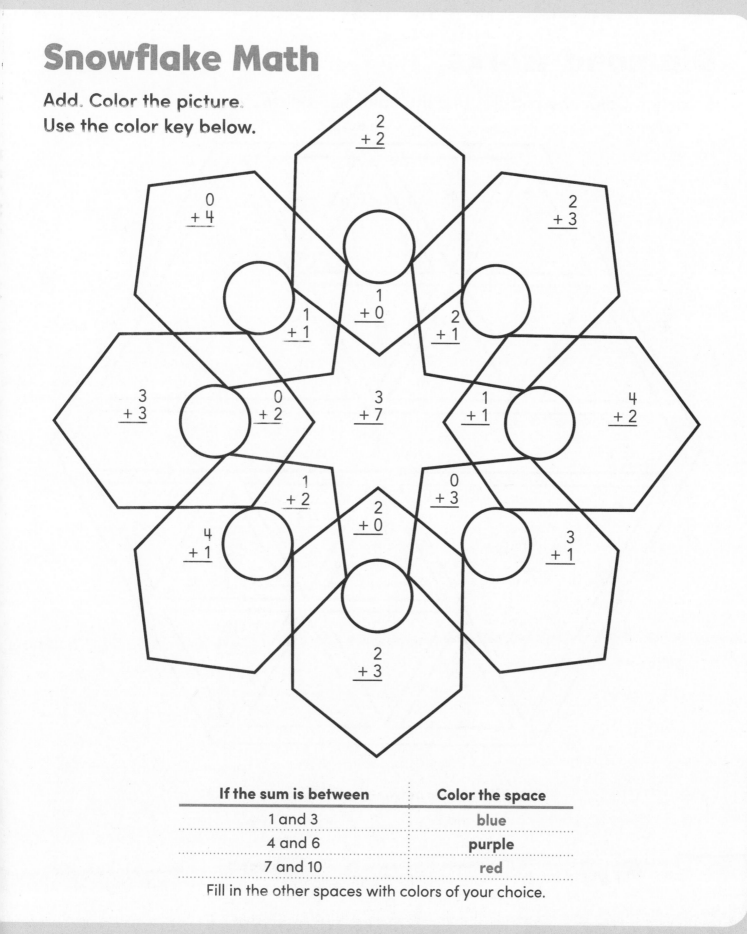

If the sum is between	Color the space
1 and 3	blue
4 and 6	purple
7 and 10	red

Fill in the other spaces with colors of your choice.

Diamond Works

Subtract. Color the picture. Use the color key below.

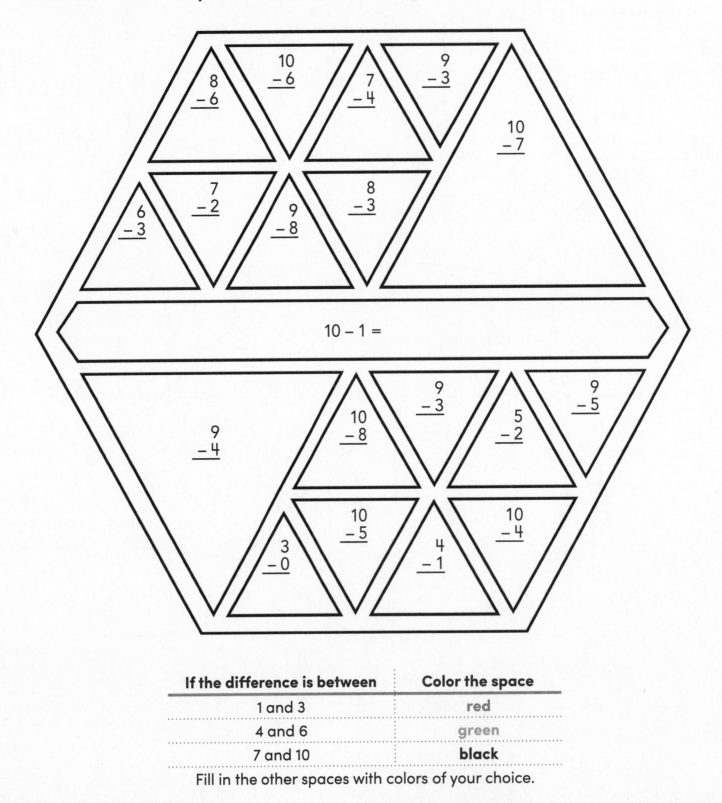

If the difference is between	Color the space
1 and 3	red
4 and 6	green
7 and 10	black

Fill in the other spaces with colors of your choice.

Juggling Act

Cross out. Write how many are left.

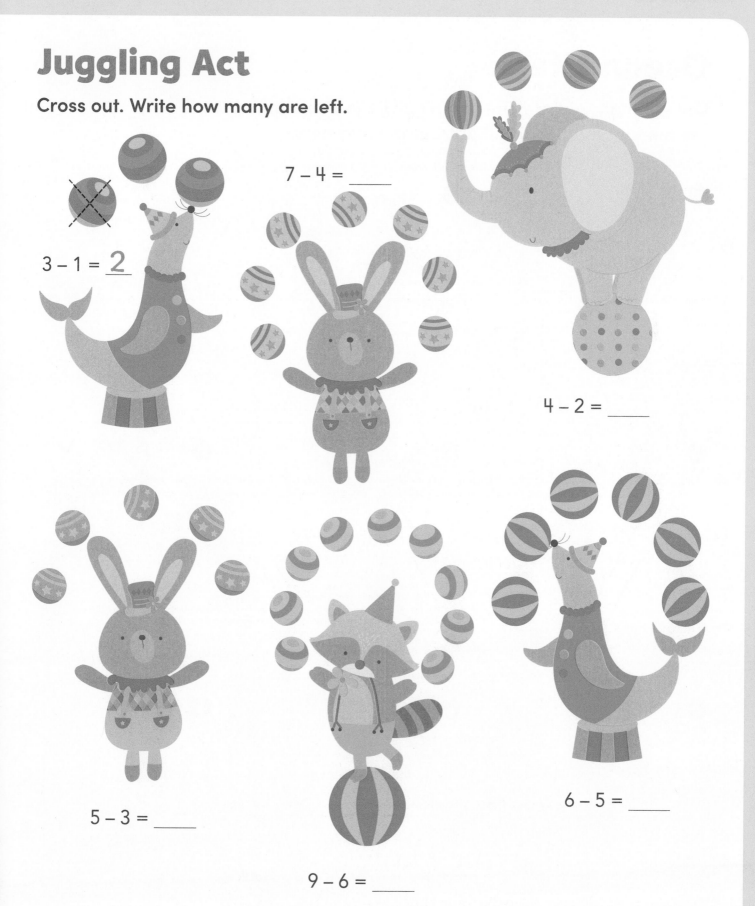

$3 - 1 = \underline{2}$

$7 - 4 = \underline{}$

$4 - 2 = \underline{}$

$5 - 3 = \underline{}$

$9 - 6 = \underline{}$

$6 - 5 = \underline{}$

Ocean Life

Use the math picture on the next page to count and write the number in each box. Subtract the numbers.

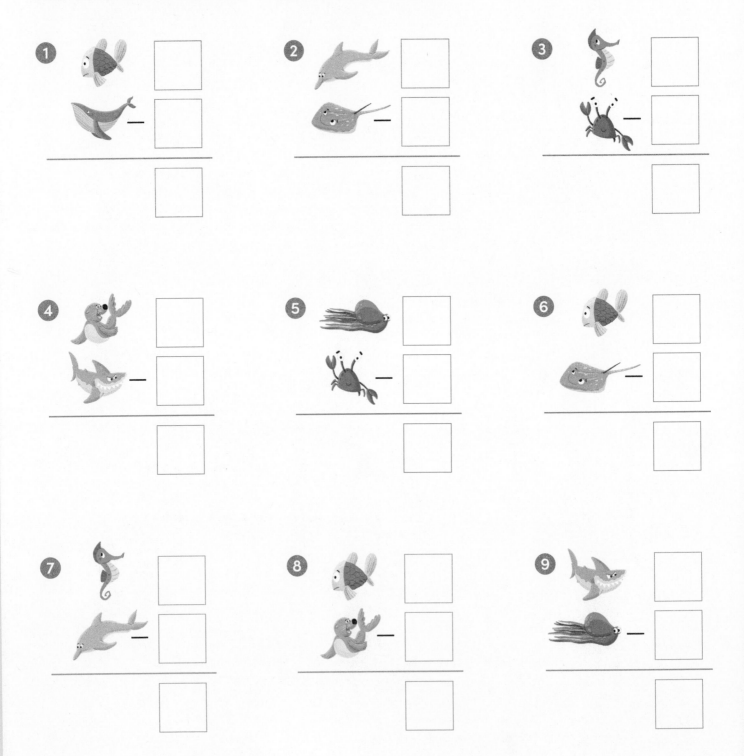

Trucking Along

Subtract. Color the picture using the Color Key.

Color Key	
0	white
1	brown
2	black
3	green
4	purple
5	orange
6	yellow
7	blue
8	red

$$9 - 2$$

$$7 - 6 =$$

$$9 - 1 =$$

$$8 - 4 =$$

$$7 - 3 =$$

$$6 - 2 =$$

$$10 - 6$$

$$9 - 5$$

$$1 - 1$$

$$5 - 2$$

$$4 - 4 =$$

$$10 - 7$$

$$10 - 4 =$$

$$10 - 2 =$$

$$8 - 2$$

$$10 - 9$$

$$6 - 3 =$$

$$9 - 7 =$$

$$9 - 4 =$$

$$9 - 3$$

$$10 - 8 =$$

$$9 - 6$$

$$7 - 5 =$$

$$8 - 2 =$$

$$4 - 3$$

$$9 - 1$$

Night Lights

Subtract.
Connect the dots from
greatest to least.

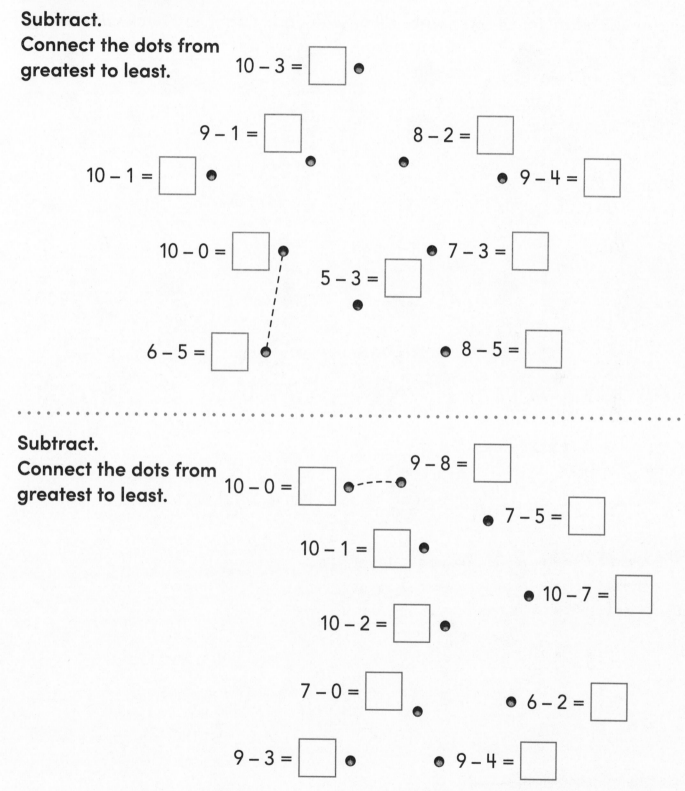

$10 - 3 =$ ⬜ •

$9 - 1 =$ ⬜

$8 - 2 =$ ⬜

$10 - 1 =$ ⬜ •

$9 - 4 =$ ⬜

$10 - 0 =$ ⬜

$7 - 3 =$ ⬜

$5 - 3 =$ ⬜

$6 - 5 =$ ⬜

$8 - 5 =$ ⬜

Subtract.
Connect the dots from
greatest to least.

$10 - 0 =$ ⬜

$9 - 8 =$ ⬜

$7 - 5 =$ ⬜

$10 - 1 =$ ⬜ •

$10 - 7 =$ ⬜

$10 - 2 =$ ⬜ •

$7 - 0 =$ ⬜

$6 - 2 =$ ⬜

$9 - 3 =$ ⬜ •

$9 - 4 =$ ⬜

Hop to It: Add and Subtract

Add or subtract. Trace the number line with your finger to check your work.

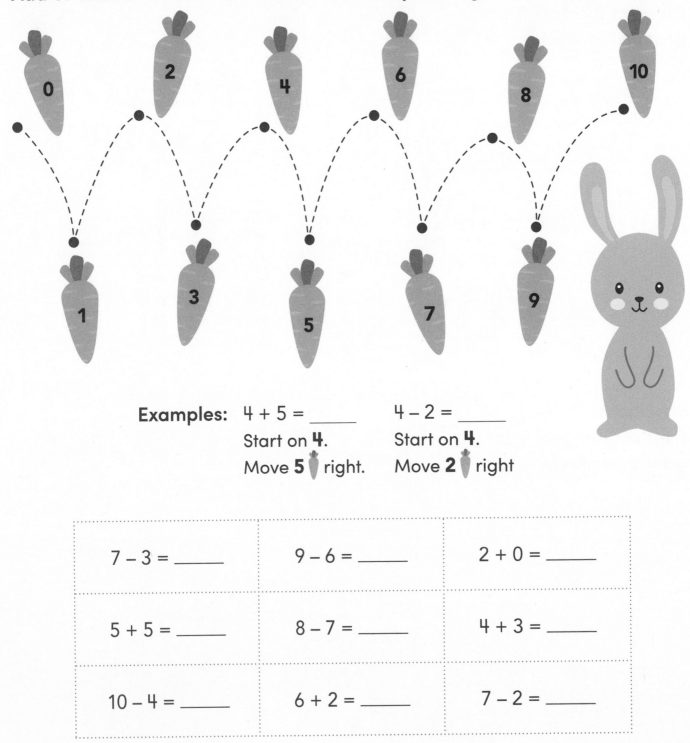

Examples: 4 + 5 = _____   4 – 2 = _____
Start on **4**.   Start on **4**.
Move **5** 🥕 right.   Move **2** 🥕 right

7 – 3 = _____	9 – 6 = _____	2 + 0 = _____
5 + 5 = _____	8 – 7 = _____	4 + 3 = _____
10 – 4 = _____	6 + 2 = _____	7 – 2 = _____

Kickboard Match Up

Add or subtract. Draw a line to match kickboards with the same answer.

Blast Off

Add or subtract. Then use the code to answer the riddle below.

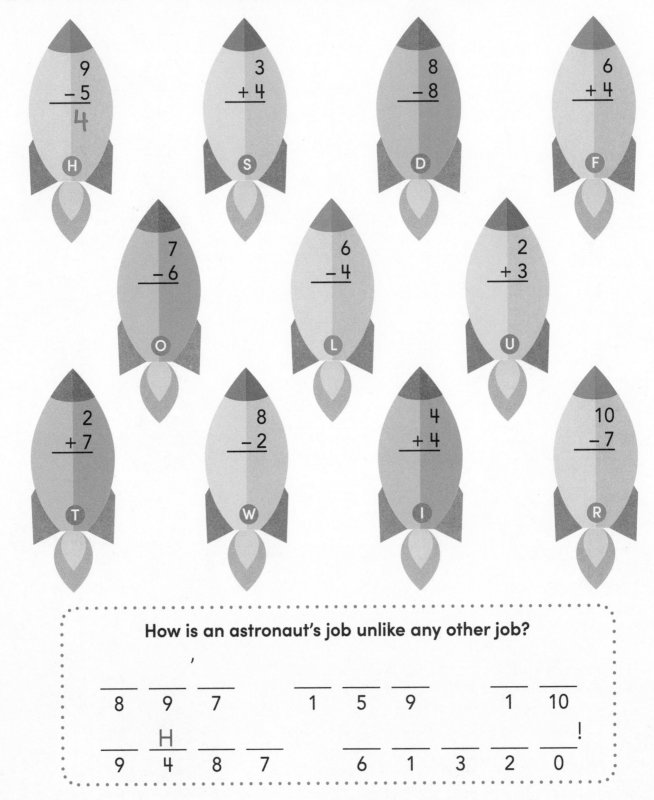

9
−5
4

H

3
+4

S

8
−8

D

6
+4

F

7
−6

O

6
−4

L

2
+3

U

2
+7

T

8
−2

W

4
+4

I

10
−7

R

How is an astronaut's job unlike any other job?

,

___ ___ ___   ___ ___ ___   ___ ___
 8   9   7   1   5   9   1   10

___ _H_ ___ ___   ___ ___ ___ ___ ___!
 9   4   8   7   6   1   3   2   0

Out on the Town

Color a box on the graph for each item in the picture.

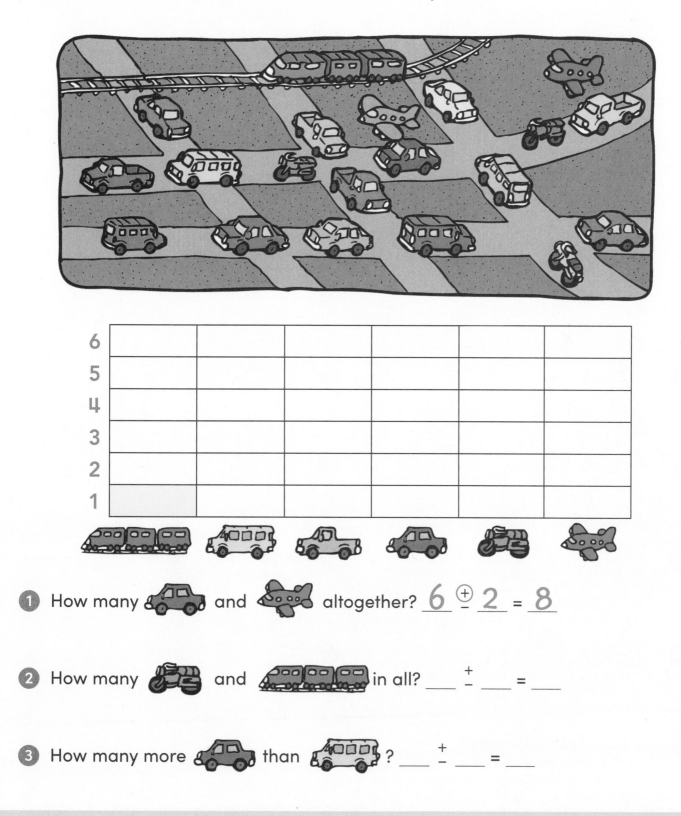

1 How many 🚗 and ✈ altogether? $6 \oplus 2 = 8$

2 How many 🏍 and 🚆 in all? ___ $\frac{+}{-}$ ___ = ___

3 How many more 🚗 than 🚐? ___ $\frac{+}{-}$ ___ = ___

Shapes on a Snake

Write the number for each shape. Add or subtract.

A ♥ + ⬭ = _____

B ⬤ − ⯃ = _____

C ▭ + ⯃ = _____

D ◆ + ⬡ = _____

E ▲ − ▭ = _____

F ▱ − ◆ = _____

G ⬭ + ♥ = _____

H ⯃ + ⬡ = _____

I ♥ + ⬭ = _____

J ▱ − ⬡ = _____

Planes... Trains...

Add or subtract

A
There are **7** cars in the parking lot. Then **3** more cars park there, too. How many cars are there in all in the lot?

$$\underline{7} \oplus \underline{3} = \underline{10} \text{ cars}$$

B
There are **7** boxes on the truck. Then **4** boxes fall on the street. How many boxes are left on the truck?

$$\underline{} \overset{+}{-} \underline{} = \underline{} \text{ boxes}$$

C
There are **10** planes waiting on the runway. Then **6** planes take off. How many planes are left on the runway?

$$\underline{} \overset{+}{-} \underline{} = \underline{} \text{ planes}$$

D
There are **8** girls and **2** boys on the bus. How many more girls than boys are on the bus?

$$\underline{} \overset{+}{-} \underline{} = \underline{} \text{ more girls}$$

E
There are **5** people in the first car and **4** people in the second car. How many people in all?

$$\underline{} \overset{+}{-} \underline{} = \underline{} \text{ people}$$

Slice It Up

Add. Color the picture using the Color Key.

Color Key

14	brown
15	green
16	red
17	yellow
18	tan

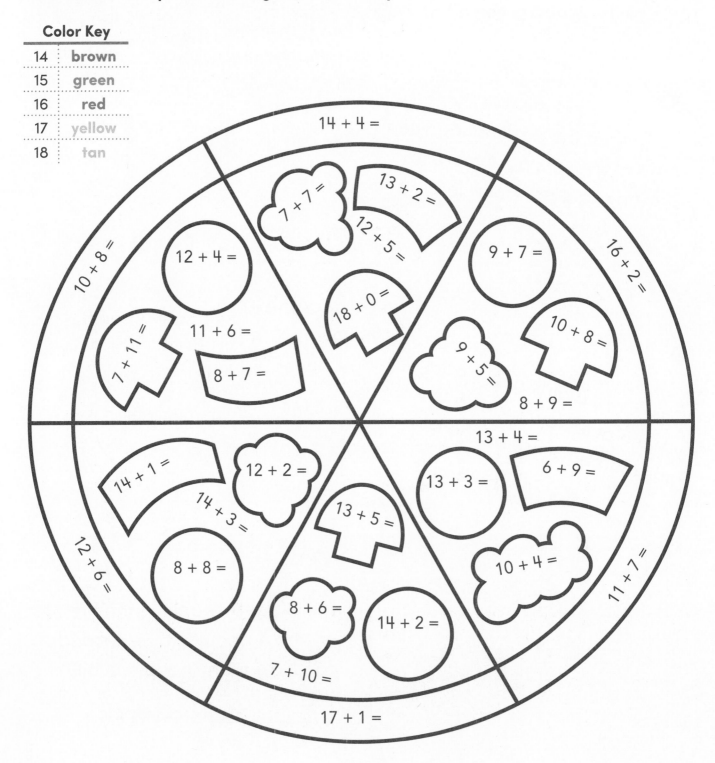

Leap on Over

Add. To show the frog's path across the pond,
color each lily pad green if the sum is greater than 10.

Gumball, Anyone?

Add. Color the picture.
Use the color key below.

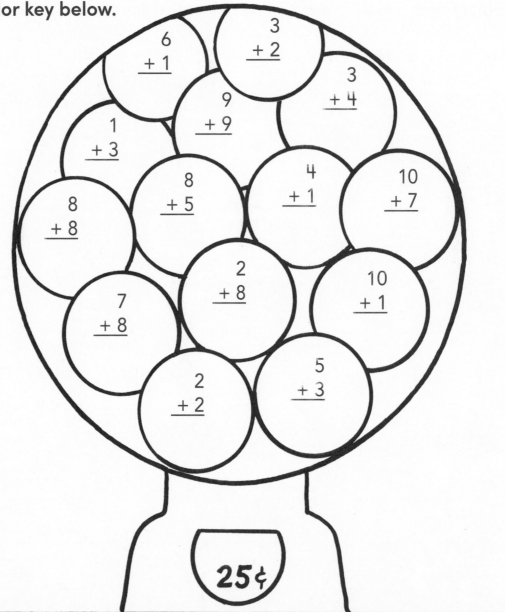

If the sum is between	Color the space
1 and 5	green
6 and 10	red
11 and 15	yellow
16 and 18	orange

Fill in the other spaces with colors of your choice.

Key Code

Add. Then use the code to answer the riddle below.

6 + 2	4 + 3	2 + 1	4 + 1
I	**D**	**H**	**A**
11 + 3	8 + 2	7 + 5	9 + 2
A	**B**	**N**	**S**
6 + 3	11 + 4	5 +13	9 + 4
O	**U**	**R**	**P**

What has 88 keys but can't open a single door?

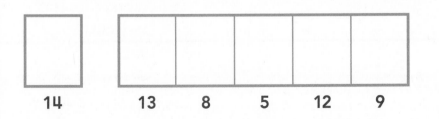

14	13	8	5	12	9

Flying High

Add down and across to find the missing number.

Kite 1:
2	4	6
3	1	4
5	5	10

Kite 2:
6	7	
2	1	

Kite 3:
4	1	
7	3	

Kite 4:
5	6	
4	3	

Kite 5:
4	7	
3	3	

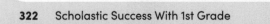

Double Dips

Write the doubles that equal the number on the cone.

⭐ Circle the answer. When adding doubles,
the sum will always be: **even**   **odd**

Not Far From Home

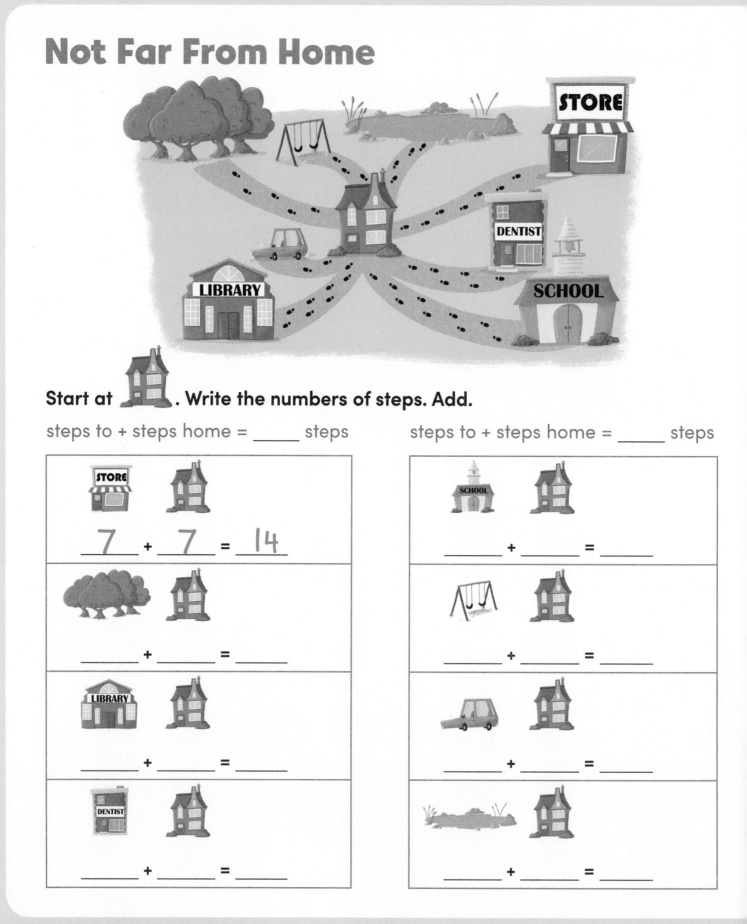

Start at 🏠. Write the numbers of steps. Add.

steps to + steps home = _____ steps   steps to + steps home = _____ steps

STORE 🏠 ___7___ + ___7___ = __14__	SCHOOL 🏠 _____ + _____ = _____
🌳 🏠 _____ + _____ = _____	🛝 🏠 _____ + _____ = _____
LIBRARY 🏠 _____ + _____ = _____	🚗 🏠 _____ + _____ = _____
DENTIST 🏠 _____ + _____ = _____	🌿 🏠 _____ + _____ = _____

Break the Code

Subtract.

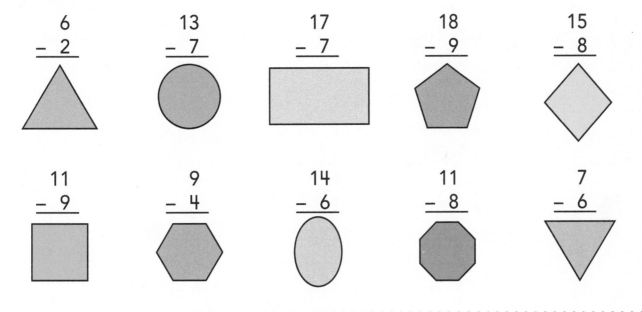

6	13	17	18	15
− 2	− 7	− 7	− 9	− 8

11	9	14	11	7
− 9	− 4	− 6	− 8	− 6

· ·

Use the answers above to solve each problem.

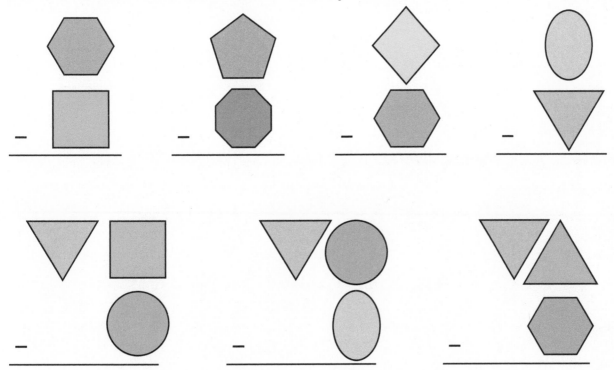

The Big Search

Subtract. Circle the difference.

11 – 7 = five three (four)	14 – 9 = nine one five
13 – 6 = six nine seven	16 – 5 = twelve thirteen eleven
18 – 9 = eleven ten nine	17 – 11 = seven six ten
15 – 5 = ten seven five	12 – 9 = three two four
12 – 4 = six eight nine	11 – 9 = three five two

Find each circled number in the word puzzle. Look → and ↓

```
(f o u r) h i o n e g s k m
 i f o n t g y f a f u e z
 f t l u e j s i x s b x t
 t t w e l v e v k s t l h
 e p n i n e w e j e r t i
 e d n g q i h r y v a q r
 n v h h o t h r e e c s t
 d m k t c w b t e n t r e
 x d i p g o a c p f i s e
 c e l e v e n a b z o v n
 b w u d i f f e r e n c e
```

See if you can find these number words: twelve, fifteen, thirteen, subtraction, difference.

Race Through the Facts

Add or subtract.
The race car that ends with the highest number wins the race!

$7 + 2 =$ _____ $- 4 =$ _____ $- 3 =$ _____ $+ 9 =$

$12 - 3 =$ _____ $- 6 =$ _____ $+ 2 =$ _____ $+ 9 =$

$+ 5 =$

$- 8 =$

$+ 4 =$ _____ $+ 7 =$ _____ $- 6 =$ _____ $+ 3 =$ _____ $+ 7 =$

$- 2 =$

$+ 4 =$ _____ $+ 6 =$ _____ $- 9 =$ _____ $+ 1 =$ _____ $+ 4 =$

$- 8 =$

$+ 7 =$

$+ 1 =$

$- 11 =$

$- 5 =$ _____ $+ 2 =$ _____ $+ 3 =$ _____ $- 3 =$

$+ 13 =$ _____ $- 7 =$ _____ $+ 3 =$

Little Snacks

Add or subtract. Then follow the maze through the even answers.

13 − 6 =

16 − 9 =

4 + 5 =

2 + 2 =

14 − 8 =

10 − 7 =

3 + 7 =

13 − 5 =

9 + 4 =

15 − 6 =

16 − 6 =

11 + 3 =

17 − 8 =

7 + 5 =

18 − 6 =

8 + 3 =

5 + 2 =

9 + 9 =

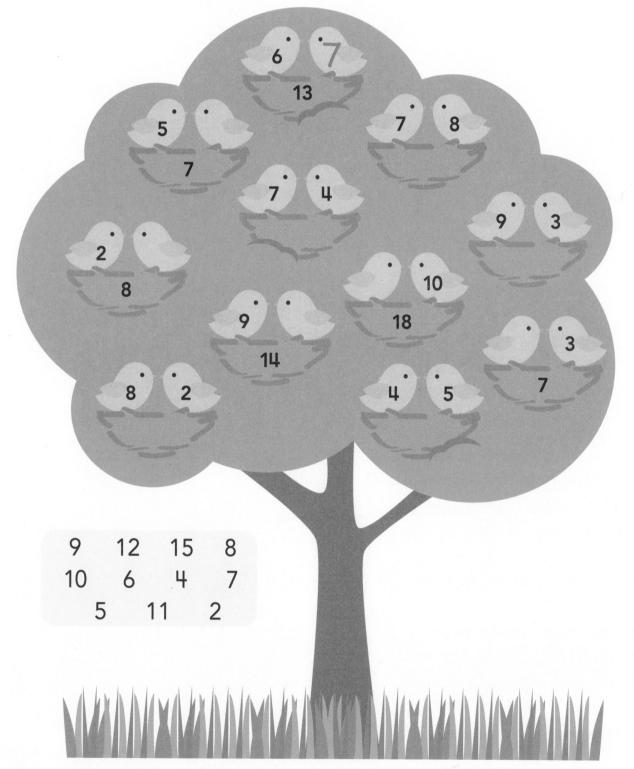

Flying Families

Fill in the missing number for each family.
Use the numbers from the box.

```
  9    12    15    8
10    6     4     7
  5    11    2
```

Colorful Flowers

Color a box on the graph for each item in the picture.

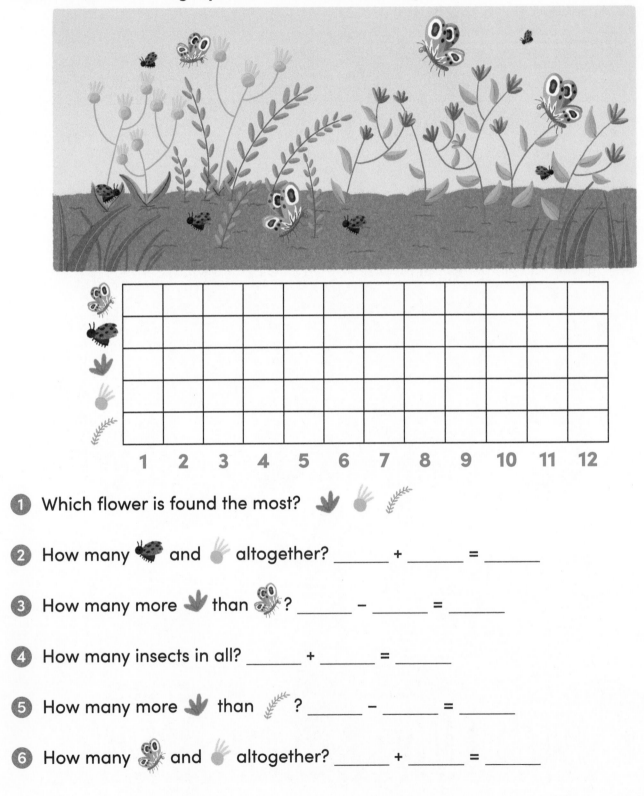

1. Which flower is found the most?

2. How many and altogether? _____ + _____ = _____

3. How many more than ? _____ − _____ = _____

4. How many insects in all? _____ + _____ = _____

5. How many more than ? _____ − _____ = _____

6. How many and altogether? _____ + _____ = _____

A Nutty Bunch

Add or subtract. Circle the nut if the answer matches the squirrel.

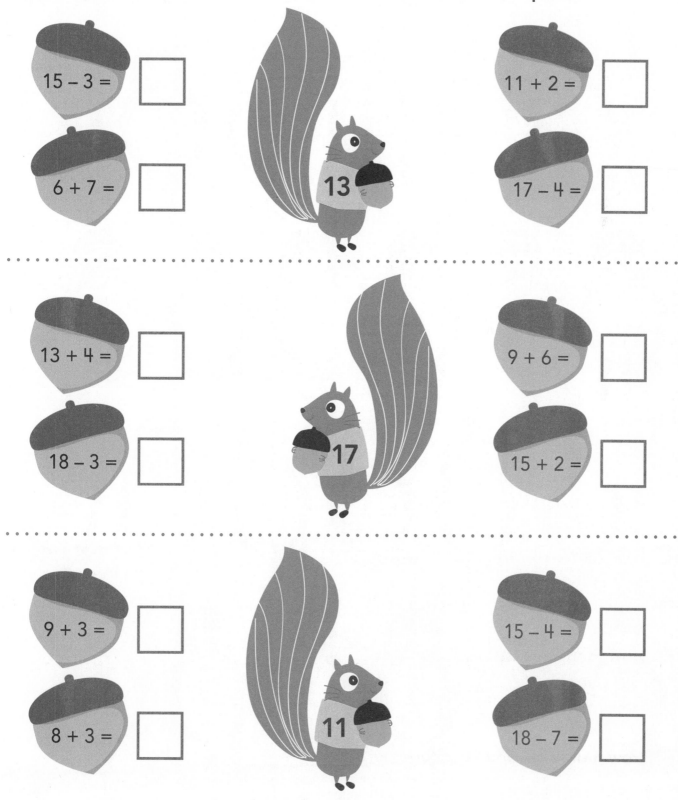

15 − 3 = ☐

6 + 7 = ☐

13

11 + 2 = ☐

17 − 4 = ☐

13 + 4 = ☐

18 − 3 = ☐

17

9 + 6 = ☐

15 + 2 = ☐

9 + 3 = ☐

8 + 3 = ☐

11

15 − 4 = ☐

18 − 7 = ☐

Penguin Parade

Add or subtract.

Row 1:
5 + 7
8 + 3
15 − 5
18 − 9
11 − 3
12 − 5

Row 2:
9 − 7
12 − 8
5 + 1
16 − 8
13 − 3
7 + 5

Row 3:
12 − 9
11 − 5
13 − 4
7 + 6
18 − 3
11 + 7

Row 4:
15 − 2
4 + 7
12 − 3
12 − 5
8 − 3
12 − 9

A Perfect Strike

Fill in the missing number.

2   1   3   **6**

9   3   **16**

4   3   **9**

5   2   **10**

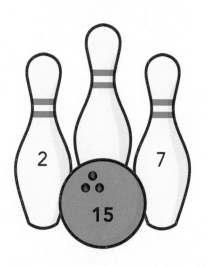
2   7   **15**

2   5   **11**

3   4   **13**

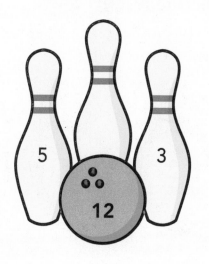
5   3   **12**

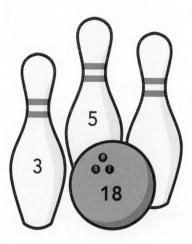
3   5   **18**

What a Treat!

Find the number in the mouse and cheese. ☐

Find the sum of the numbers in the cheese.

_____ + _____ + _____ = _____

Find the sum of the numbers in the mouse.

_____ + _____ + _____ = _____

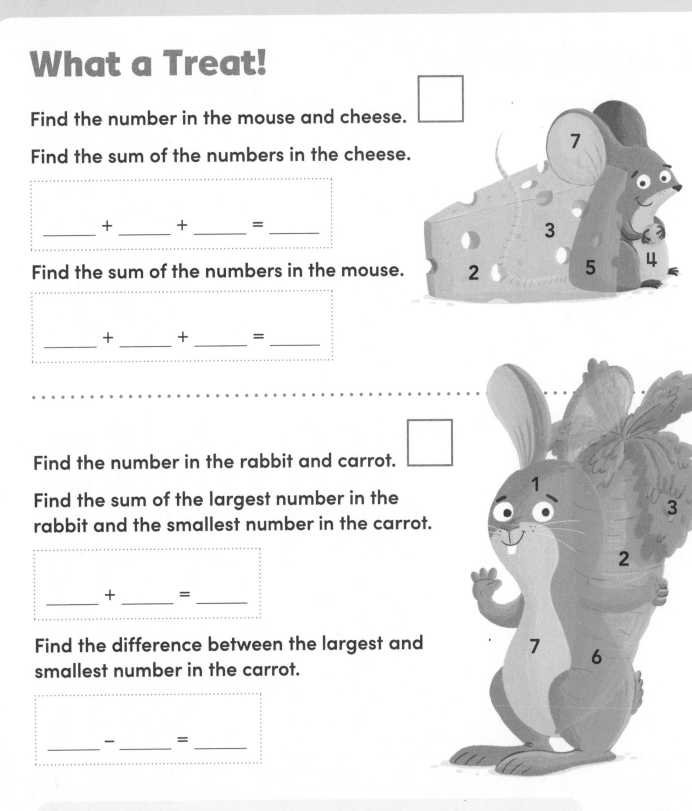

Find the number in the rabbit and carrot. ☐

Find the sum of the largest number in the rabbit and the smallest number in the carrot.

_____ + _____ = _____

Find the difference between the largest and smallest number in the carrot.

_____ - _____ = _____

☆ Find the sum of all the numbers in the cheese and carrot.

_____ + _____ + _____ + _____ + _____ = _____

Have a Heart

Circle a group of 10. Write the number of tens and ones.

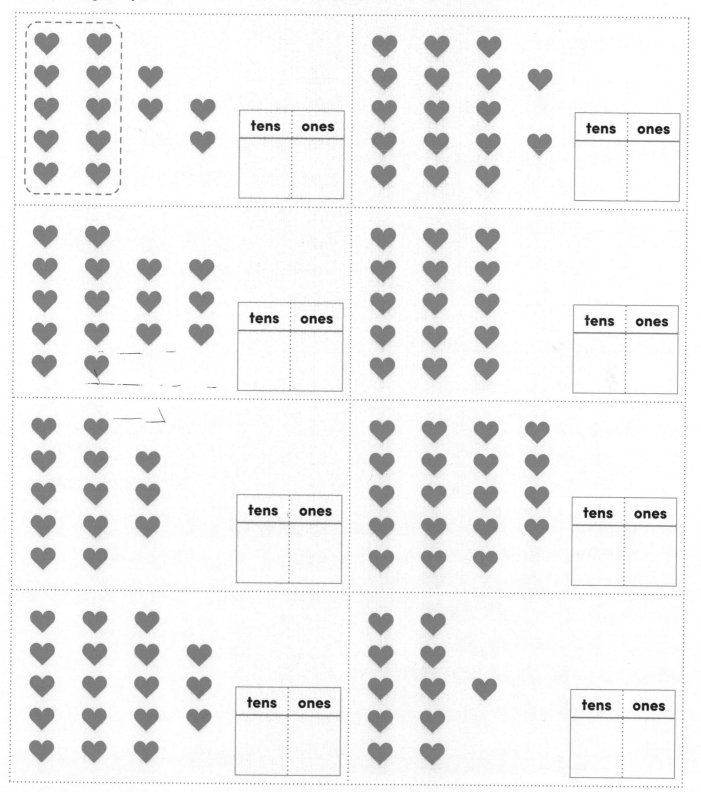

So Many Flowers!

Count. Circle groups of 10. Write the number of tens and ones.

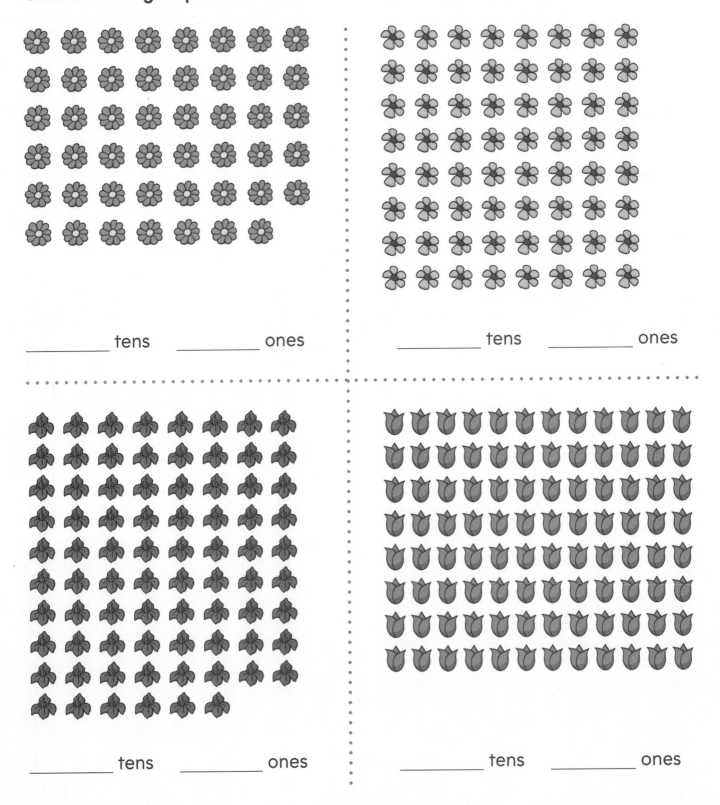

_____ tens   _____ ones

_____ tens   _____ ones

_____ tens   _____ ones

_____ tens   _____ ones

Counting Blocks

How many blocks? Write the number.

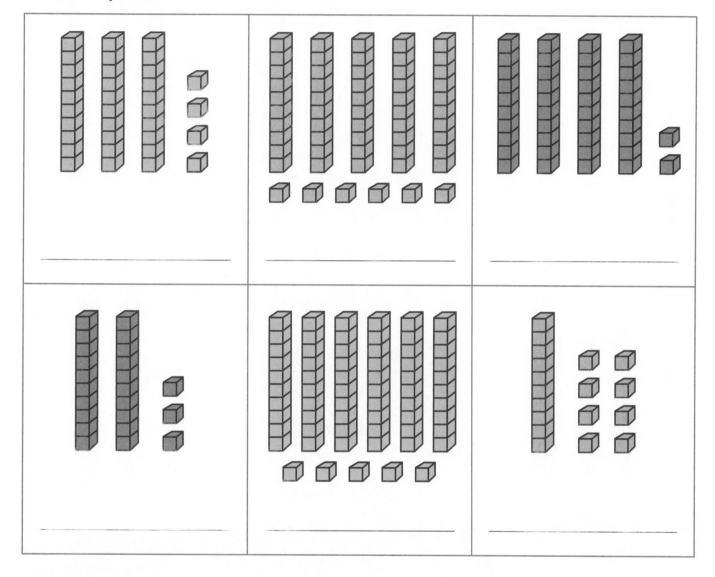

Write the number.

Tens	Ones
9	1

Tens	Ones
7	3

Tens	Ones
6	8

Beautiful Butterflies

Add. Color the picture using the Color Key.

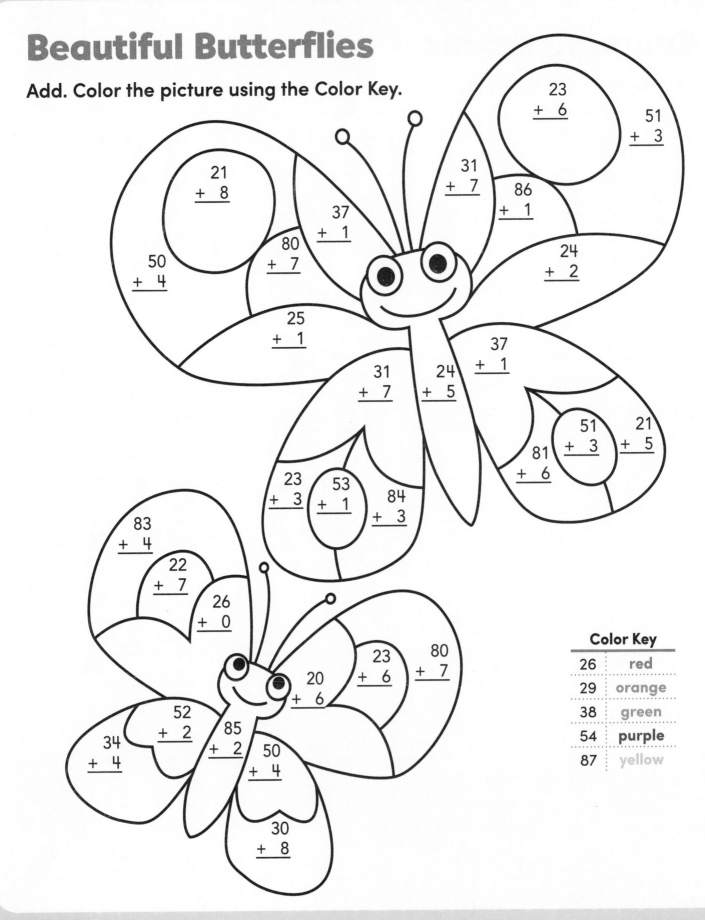

Color Key	
26	red
29	orange
38	green
54	purple
87	yellow

© Scholastic Inc.

Where's the Beach?

Add. To find the path to the beach,
color each box with an odd answer yellow.

14 + 3	34 + 2	81 + 3

76 + 2	25 + 4	56 + 3	11 + 3	40 + 8
87 + 1	22 + 2	32 + 3	65 + 1	93 + 5
10 + 8	41 + 2	70 + 7	32 + 6	84 + 4
73 + 5	63 + 2	55 + 1	41 + 5	23 + 3

98 + 1	53 + 4	82 + 5

By the Seashore

Use the code below to write each missing number. Add.

93
+

82
+

14
+

21
+

53
+

45
+

73
+

36
+

61
+

32
+

Sail Away

Find each addition sentence. Add.
Then, fill in the empty flag!

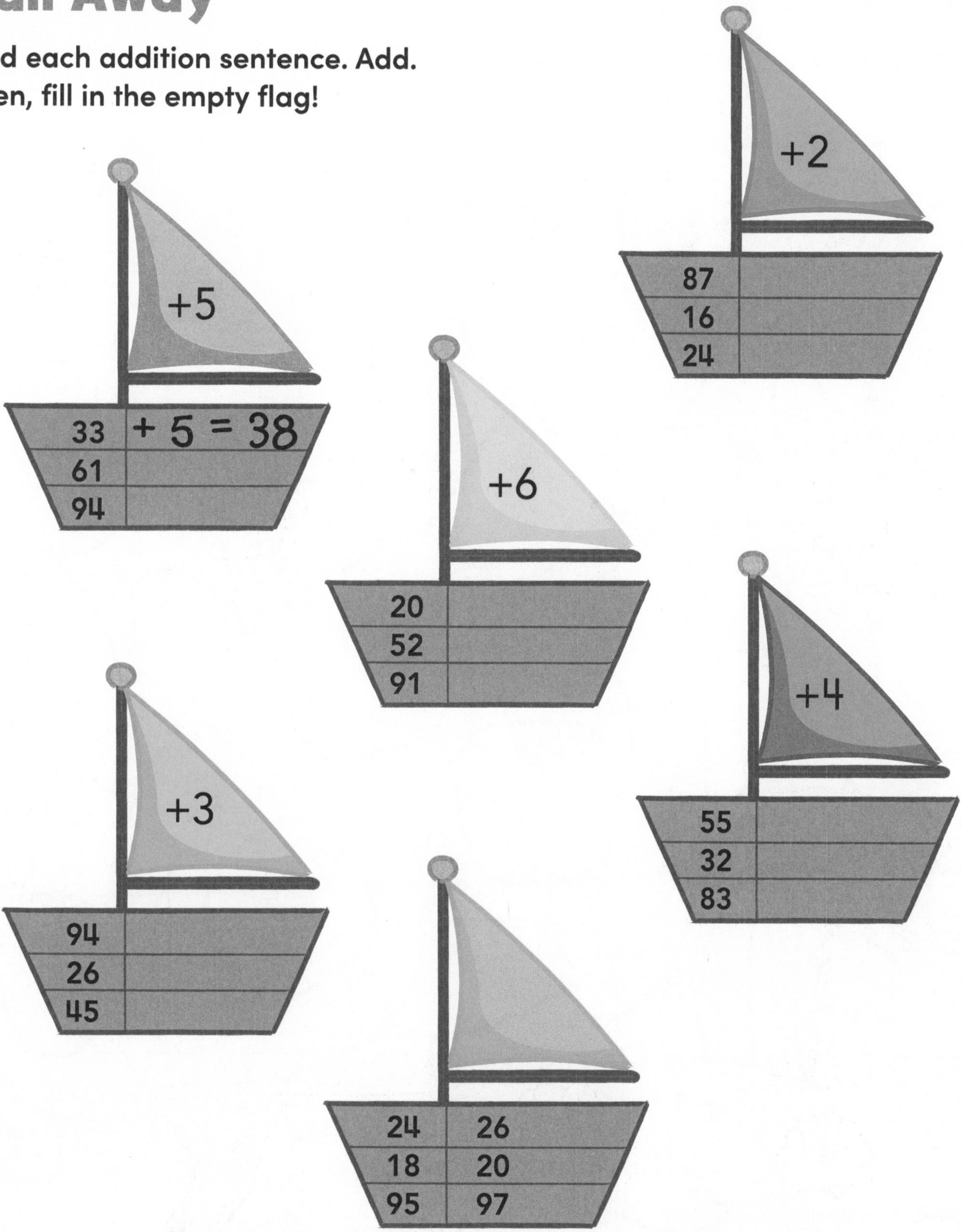

+5

33	+ 5 = 38
61	
94	

+2

87	
16	
24	

+6

20	
52	
91	

+3

94	
26	
45	

+4

55	
32	
83	

24	26
18	20
95	97

Dino-Math

Subtract. Color the picture using the Color Key.

Color Key

16	red
22	orange
34	purple
57	blue
73	yellow
85	green

Butterfly Friends

Subtract. Remember: the larger number always goes on top!

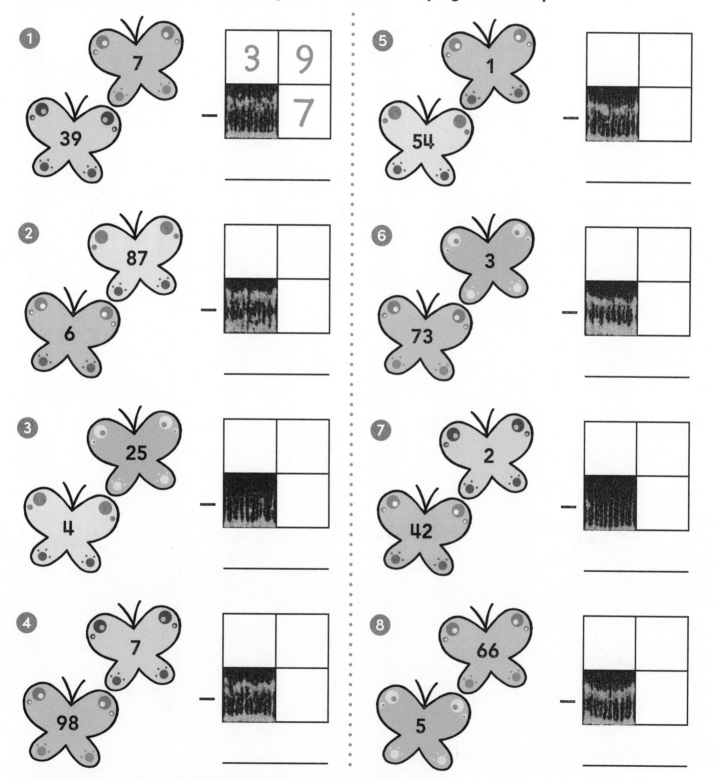

1) 7   39

	3	9
−		7

5) 1   54

2) 87   6

6) 3   73

3) 25   4

7) 2   42

4) 7   98

8) 66   5

Treasure Island

Subtract.

43 – 1	95 – 5	79 – 3	36 – 4	89 – 7	66 – 3	83 – 2
59 – 9	37 – 2	24 – 3	27 – 6	42 – 1	90 – 0	55 – 2
33 – 3	84 – 4	28 – 8	71 – 1	62 – 2	68 – 3	77 – 3

**Use the clues to find the gold, the ship,
and the treasure in the boxes above.**

Find the gold. The difference is greater than **50** and less than **55**.
Color the box with the gold yellow.

Find the ship. The difference is
greater than **30** and less than **35**.
Color the box with the ship orange.

Find the sunken treasure. The
difference is greater than **70** and
less than **75**. Color the box with the
treasure red.

Riding on Air

Add. Color the picture using the Color Key.

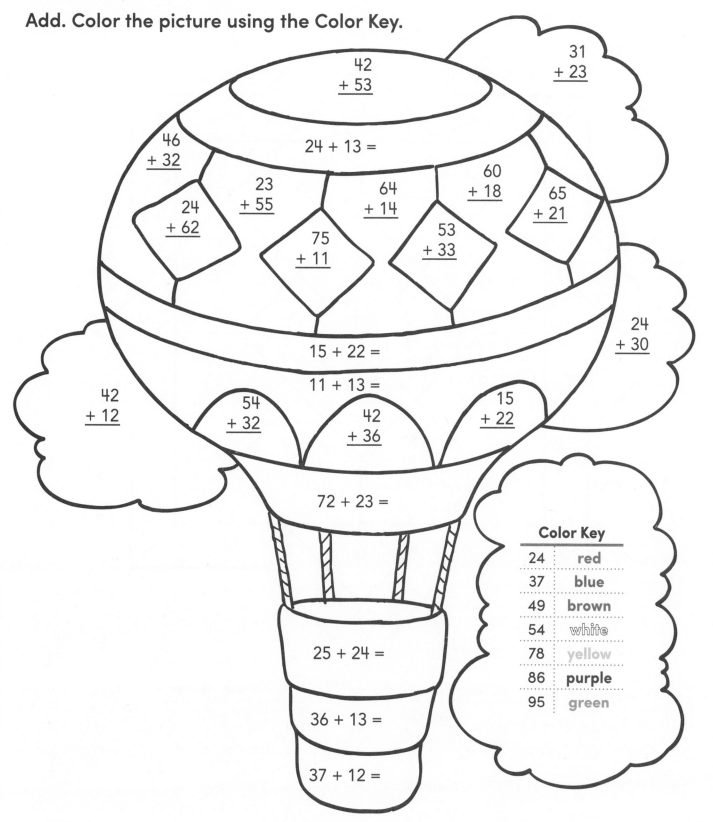

Color Key	
24	red
37	blue
49	brown
54	white
78	yellow
86	purple
95	green

Star Math

Add. Color the picture.
Use the color key below.

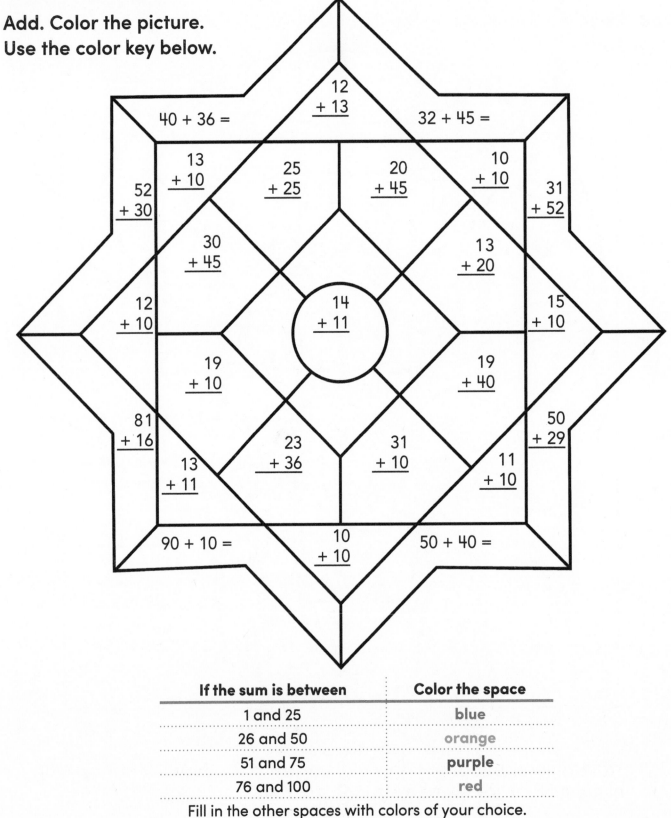

If the sum is between	Color the space
1 and 25	blue
26 and 50	orange
51 and 75	purple
76 and 100	red

Fill in the other spaces with colors of your choice.

© Scholastic Inc.

Sunflower Math

Do the addition problems in the sunflower picture below.
Then use the Color Key to color each answer.

Color Key	
56	green
68	orange
89	yellow
97	blue

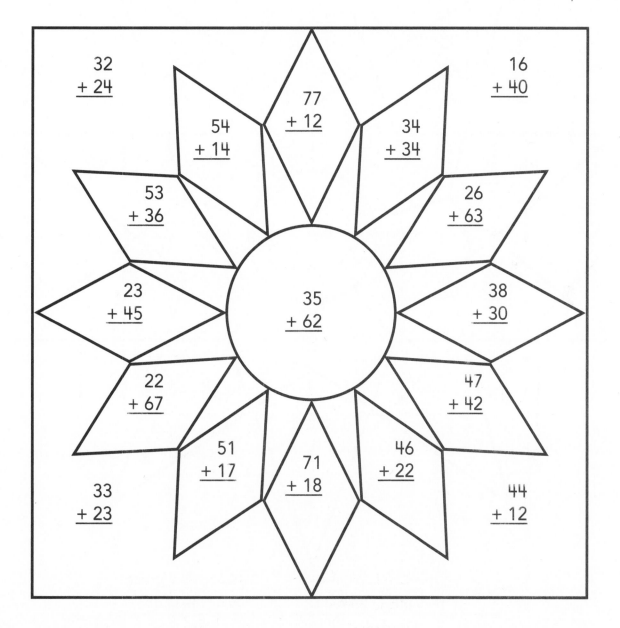

32
+ 24

77
+ 12

16
+ 40

54
+ 14

34
+ 34

53
+ 36

26
+ 63

23
+ 45

35
+ 62

38
+ 30

22
+ 67

47
+ 42

51
+ 17

46
+ 22

33
+ 23

71
+ 18

44
+ 12

⭐ Write your age on strips of paper. Then add a 6, 7, 8, and 9 to each strip
of paper. Practice the answers with a friend.

Ten-Point Star

**Add. Color the picture.
Use the color key below.**

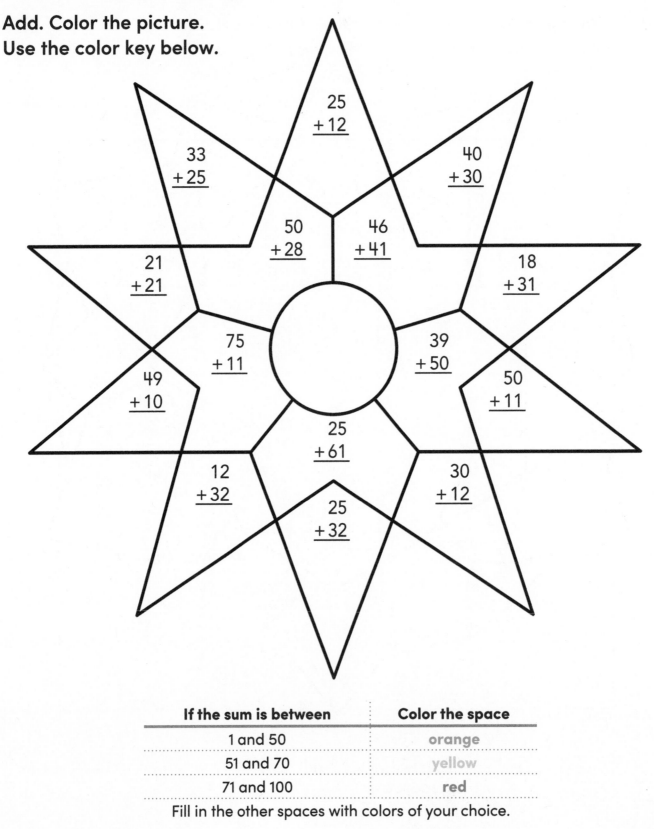

If the sum is between	Color the space
1 and 50	orange
51 and 70	yellow
71 and 100	red

Fill in the other spaces with colors of your choice.

Designer Diamond

Add. Color the picture.
Use the color key below.

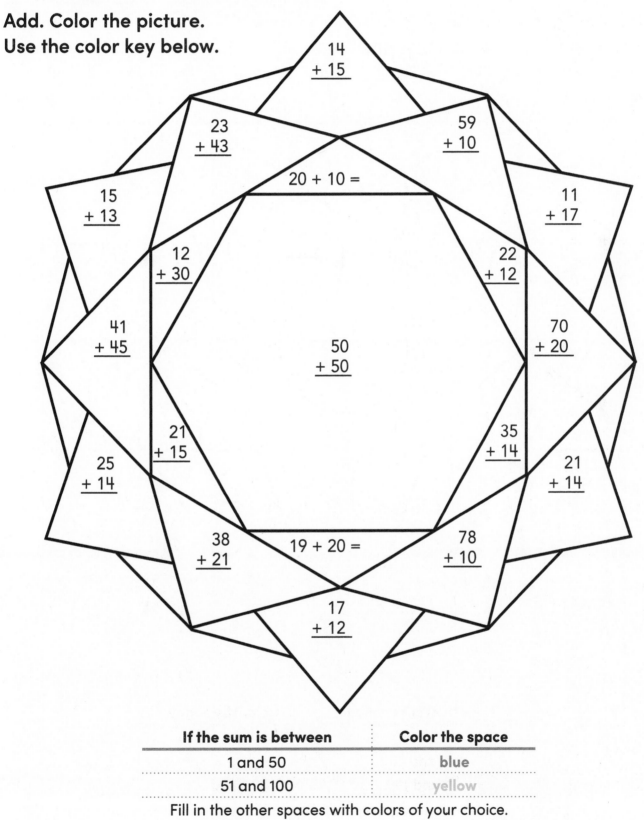

If the sum is between	Color the space
1 and 50	blue
51 and 100	yellow

Fill in the other spaces with colors of your choice.

Color the Bow

Do the subtraction problems in the picture below.
Then use the Color Key to color each answer.

Color Key	
14	red
26	purple
33	blue
47	yellow
63	green

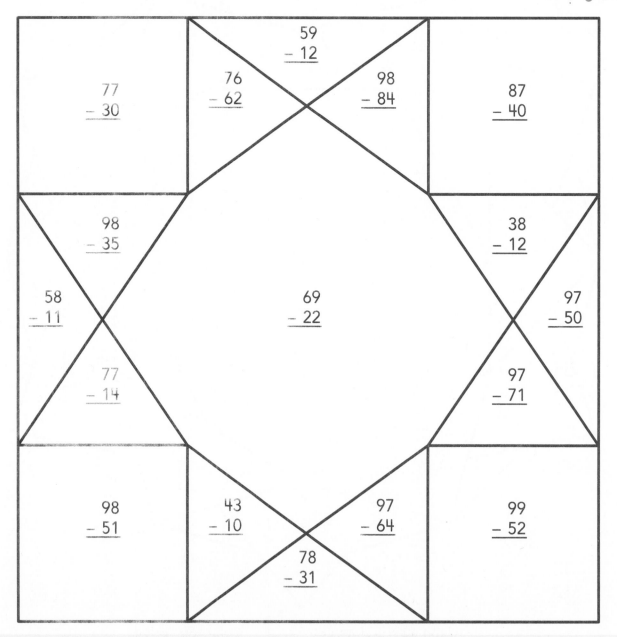

On another sheet of paper, draw a picture of four of your friends
or family members. Give each one a ribbon with a bow.

Have a Ball

Subtract.

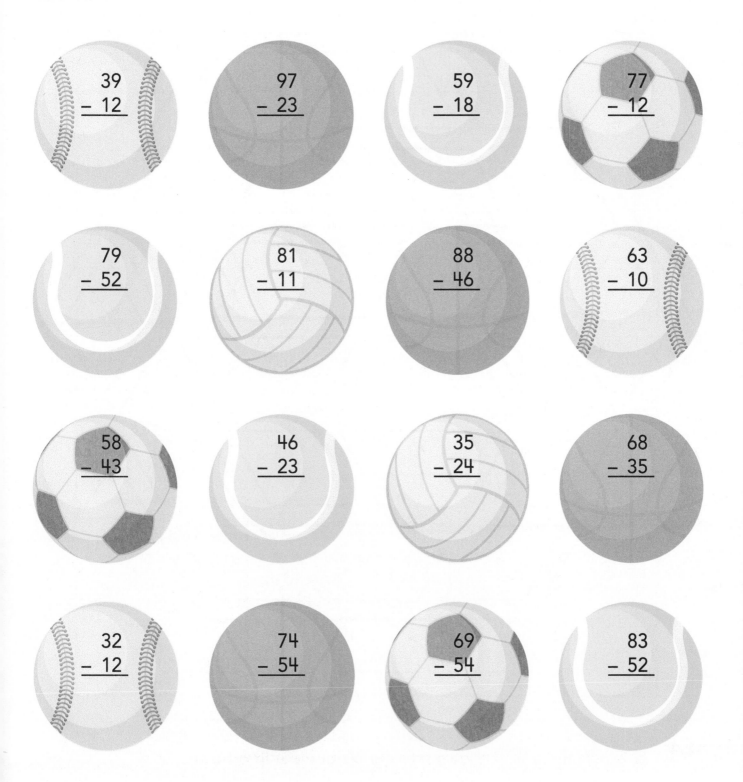

$$\begin{array}{r} 39 \\ -\ 12 \\ \hline \end{array}$$

$$\begin{array}{r} 97 \\ -\ 23 \\ \hline \end{array}$$

$$\begin{array}{r} 59 \\ -\ 18 \\ \hline \end{array}$$

$$\begin{array}{r} 77 \\ -\ 12 \\ \hline \end{array}$$

$$\begin{array}{r} 79 \\ -\ 52 \\ \hline \end{array}$$

$$\begin{array}{r} 81 \\ -\ 11 \\ \hline \end{array}$$

$$\begin{array}{r} 88 \\ -\ 46 \\ \hline \end{array}$$

$$\begin{array}{r} 63 \\ -\ 10 \\ \hline \end{array}$$

$$\begin{array}{r} 58 \\ -\ 43 \\ \hline \end{array}$$

$$\begin{array}{r} 46 \\ -\ 23 \\ \hline \end{array}$$

$$\begin{array}{r} 35 \\ -\ 24 \\ \hline \end{array}$$

$$\begin{array}{r} 68 \\ -\ 35 \\ \hline \end{array}$$

$$\begin{array}{r} 32 \\ -\ 12 \\ \hline \end{array}$$

$$\begin{array}{r} 74 \\ -\ 54 \\ \hline \end{array}$$

$$\begin{array}{r} 69 \\ -\ 54 \\ \hline \end{array}$$

$$\begin{array}{r} 83 \\ -\ 52 \\ \hline \end{array}$$

Amazing Maze

Subtract. Color the picture. Use the color key below.

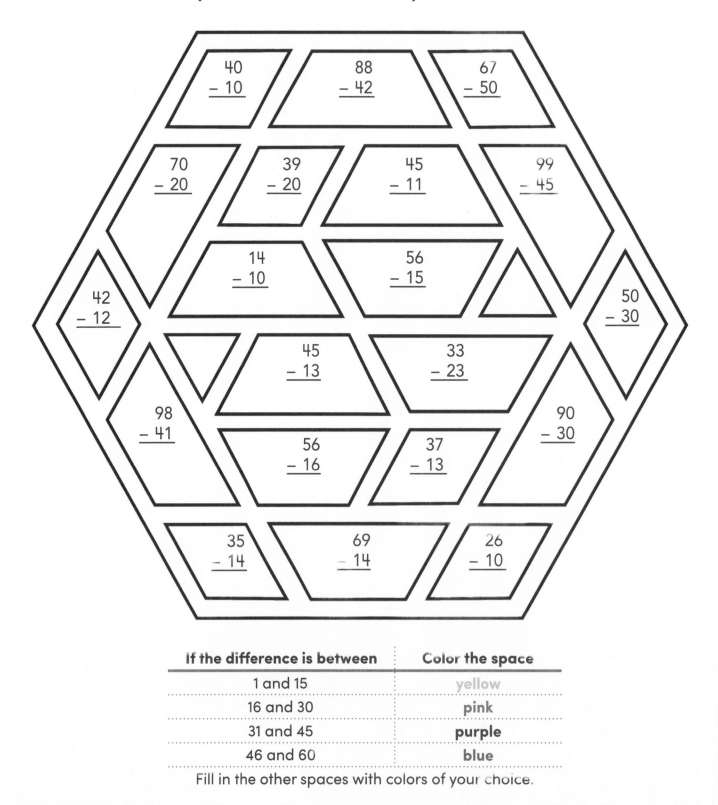

If the difference is between	Color the space
1 and 15	yellow
16 and 30	pink
31 and 45	**purple**
46 and 60	blue

Fill in the other spaces with colors of your choice.

Opposites Attract

Add or subtract. Draw a line to connect the magnets with the same answer.
Read the words in each connecting set of magnets.

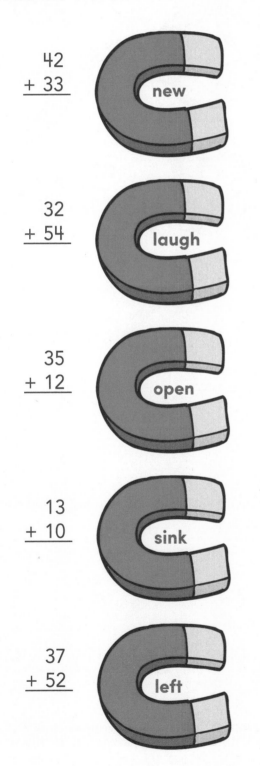
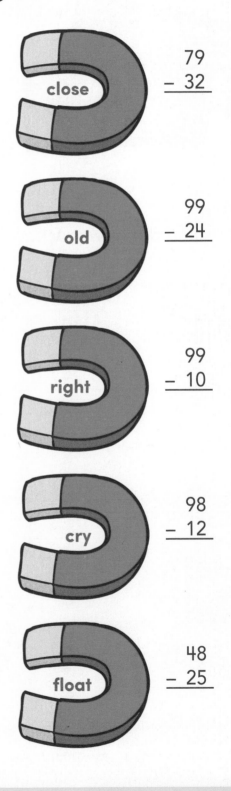

42
+ 33

new

79
− 32

close

32
+ 54

laugh

99
− 24

old

35
+ 12

open

99
− 10

right

13
+ 10

sink

98
− 12

cry

37
+ 52

left

48
− 25

float

How Much Money?

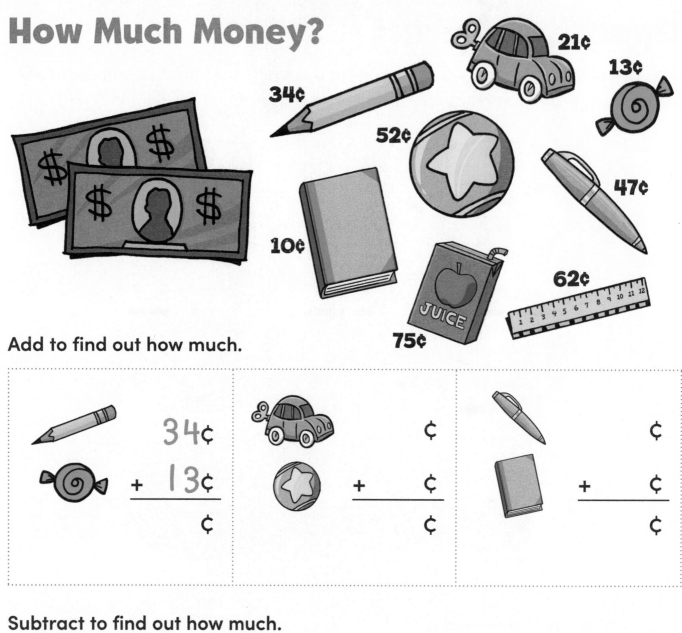

Add to find out how much.

$$34¢$$
$$+ 13¢$$
$$\overline{}¢$$

$$¢$$
$$+ ¢$$
$$\overline{}¢$$

$$¢$$
$$+ ¢$$
$$\overline{}¢$$

Subtract to find out how much.

$$¢$$
$$- ¢$$
$$\overline{}¢$$

$$¢$$
$$- ¢$$
$$\overline{}¢$$

$$¢$$
$$- ¢$$
$$\overline{}¢$$

Going to Market

| 24¢ | 38¢ | 56¢ |
| 25¢ | 72¢ | 49¢ | 50¢ |

Add to find out how much.

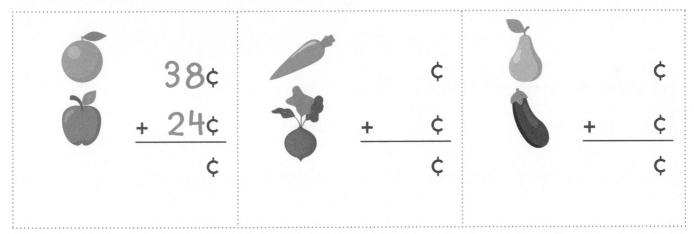

Subtract to find out how much.

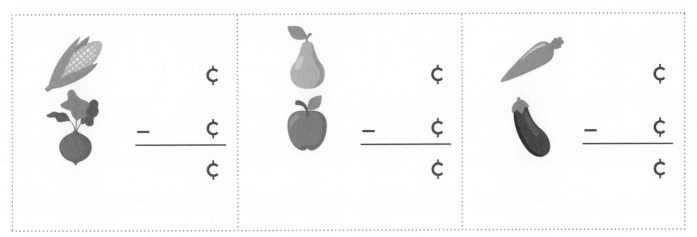

Snuggle Up With a Book

Day of the Week	Reading Minutes
Sunday	97
Monday	28
Tuesday	73
Wednesday	44
Thursday	51
Friday	45
Saturday	80

Use the chart to answer the questions.

1 What day did Alex read for the longest time? _____

2 How many minutes did Alex read on Wednesday and Friday? _____ minutes

3 What day did Alex read for the shortest time? _____

4 How many more minutes did Alex read on Sunday than Tuesday?

_____ minutes

5 How many minutes did Alex read on Monday and Thursday? _____ minutes

6 How many more minutes did Alex read on Tuesday than Thursday?

_____ minutes

Let the Sun Shine

Add or subtract. Then use the code to fill in the letters
to finish each sun fact.

13	26	34	42	57	63	71	76	85	88
f	a	s	g	r	e	l	h	t	i

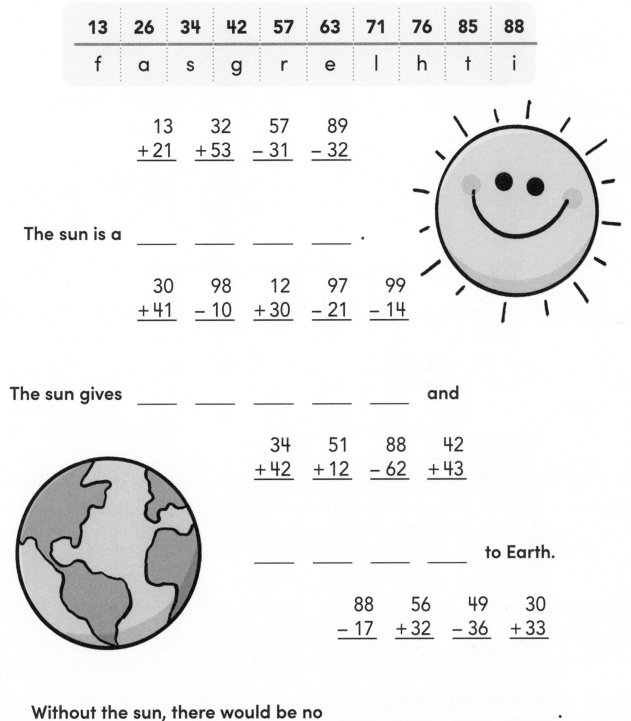

$$13 \atop +21 \qquad 32 \atop +53 \qquad 57 \atop -31 \qquad 89 \atop -32$$

The sun is a ____ ____ ____ ____ .

$$30 \atop +41 \qquad 98 \atop -10 \qquad 12 \atop +30 \qquad 97 \atop -21 \qquad 99 \atop -14$$

The sun gives ____ ____ ____ ____ ____ and

$$34 \atop +42 \qquad 51 \atop +12 \qquad 88 \atop -62 \qquad 42 \atop +43$$

____ ____ ____ ____ to Earth.

$$88 \atop -17 \qquad 56 \atop +32 \qquad 49 \atop -36 \qquad 30 \atop +33$$

Without the sun, there would be no ____ ____ ____ ____ .

Animal Surprises

Add or subtract. Match the answer to the animal fact.

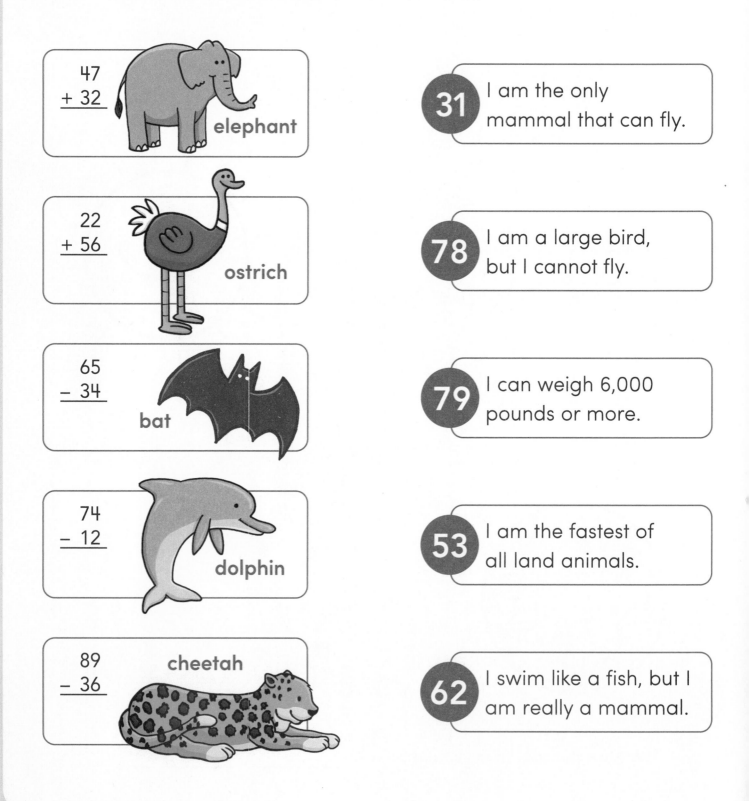

47
+ 32

elephant

22
+ 56

ostrich

65
− 34

bat

74
− 12

dolphin

89
− 36

cheetah

31 I am the only mammal that can fly.

78 I am a large bird, but I cannot fly.

79 I can weigh 6,000 pounds or more.

53 I am the fastest of all land animals.

62 I swim like a fish, but I am really a mammal.

Fishbowl Families

Add or subtract. Circle the fish that does not belong with the family.
Hint: Look at the tens place.

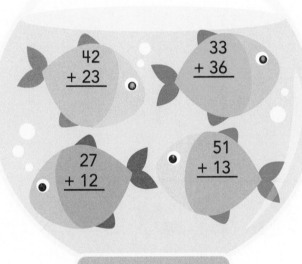

42
+ 23

33
+ 36

27
+ 12

51
+ 13

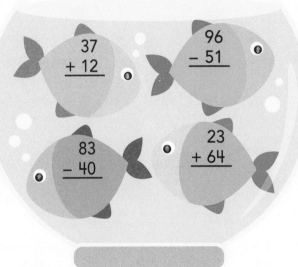

37
+ 12

96
− 51

83
− 40

23
+ 64

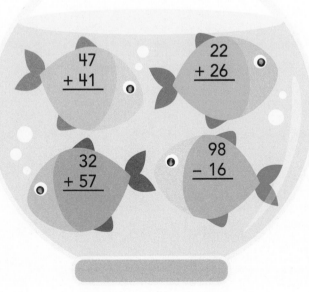

47
+ 41

22
+ 26

32
+ 57

98
− 16

 Make another family
with 7 in the tens place.

All Kinds of Patterns!

Look at the patterns below.
What do you notice about each?
Write it on the line below the pattern.

A **pattern** is something that repeats in a regular way. A pattern can include numbers, pictures, or shapes.

1 △ ◯ ⬡ △ ◯ ⬡ △ ◯ ⬡

_____

2 ⬭ ★ ◼ ⬭ ★ ◼ ⬭ ★ ◼

_____

3 ◔ ◔ ◔ ◔ ◔ ◔ ◔ ◔ ◔

_____

4 10 5 6 11 6 7 12 7 8 13 8 9

_____

Create your own pattern in the space below.

More Patterns

Add the missing numbers, letters, or symbols to each pattern.

1 ZYX WVU _____ QPO _____ KJI HGF

2 ★ _____ ☐ ☐ ★ ★ ◆ ◆ ★ ★ ☐ ☐ ★ ★ _____ ◆

3 5 20 35 _____ 65 80 95 110 125 _____

4 12 24 36 48 60 _____ 84 96 _____ 120

5 ✳ ◇ ■ ○ _____ ◇ ■ ○ ✳ ◇ _____ ○ ✳ ◇ ■ ○

6 ac _____ gi jl mo _____ su vx

7 2 4 6 10 16 _____ 42 _____ 110 178

8 ← ← ↓ ↓ → → _____ ↓ ↓ → → ← ← _____ → →

Picking Out Patterns

On the 100th day of school, everyone in Pat's class picked out patterns on the 100 Chart. Look at the chart below.

1	2	3	4	5	6	7	8	9	10
11	12	13	14	15	16	17	18	19	20
21	22	23	24	25	26	27	28	29	30
31	32	33	34	35	36	37	38	39	40
41	42	43	44	45	46	47	48	49	50
51	52	53	54	55	56	57	58	59	60
61	62	63	64	65	66	67	68	69	70
71	72	73	74	75	76	77	78	79	80
81	82	83	84	85	86	87	88	89	90
91	92	93	94	95	96	97	98	99	100

1 Find and finish the pattern starting with 2, 12, 22.

_____

2 Find and finish the pattern starting with 100, 90, 80.

_____

3 Find and finish the pattern starting with 97, 87, 77.

_____

4 Find and finish the pattern starting with 11, 22, 33.

_____

Odd and Even Patterns

A pattern can have two things repeating. This is called an "AB" pattern.

1 Look around the room. What "AB" patterns do you see?
Draw one "AB" pattern in the box.

2 Use red and blue crayons to color the numbers
in the chart using an "AB" pattern.

Hundred's Chart

1	2	3	4	5	6	7	8	9	10
11	12	13	14	15	16	17	18	19	20
21	22	23	24	25	26	27	28	29	30
31	32	33	34	35	36	37	38	39	40
41	42	43	44	45	46	47	48	49	50
51	52	53	54	55	56	57	58	59	60
61	62	63	64	65	66	67	68	69	70
71	72	73	74	75	76	77	78	79	80
81	82	83	84	85	86	87	88	89	90
91	92	93	94	95	96	97	98	99	100

Use this rule:

1 = red
2 = blue
3 = red
4 = blue, and so on

The blue numbers are **even numbers**. They can be split evenly into 2 whole numbers.

The red numbers are **odd numbers**. They cannot be split evenly into 2 whole numbers.

Odds or Evens?

Look at the numbers in the cloud.
Four are ODD. Four are EVEN.
Write the numbers in the chart.

ODD Numbers	EVEN Numbers

Color ODD numbers BLUE.
Color EVEN numbers RED.

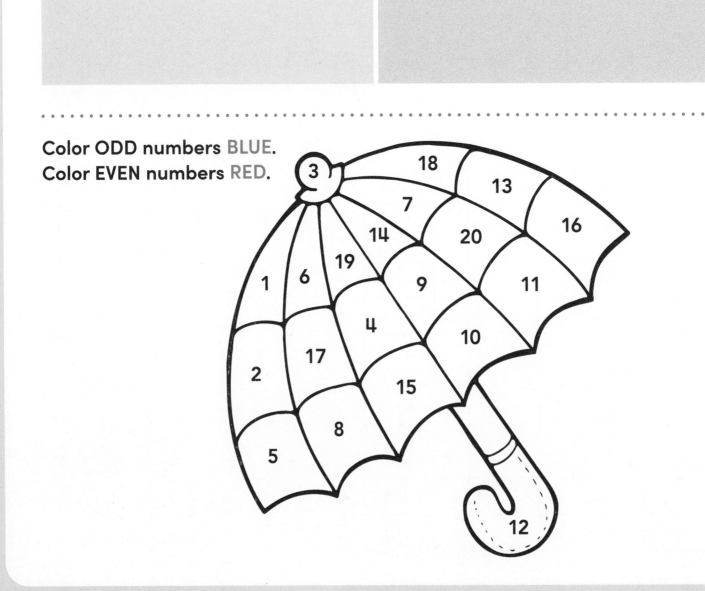

© Scholastic Inc.

Dancing Bear

Connect the dots from 20 to 60. Then color the picture.

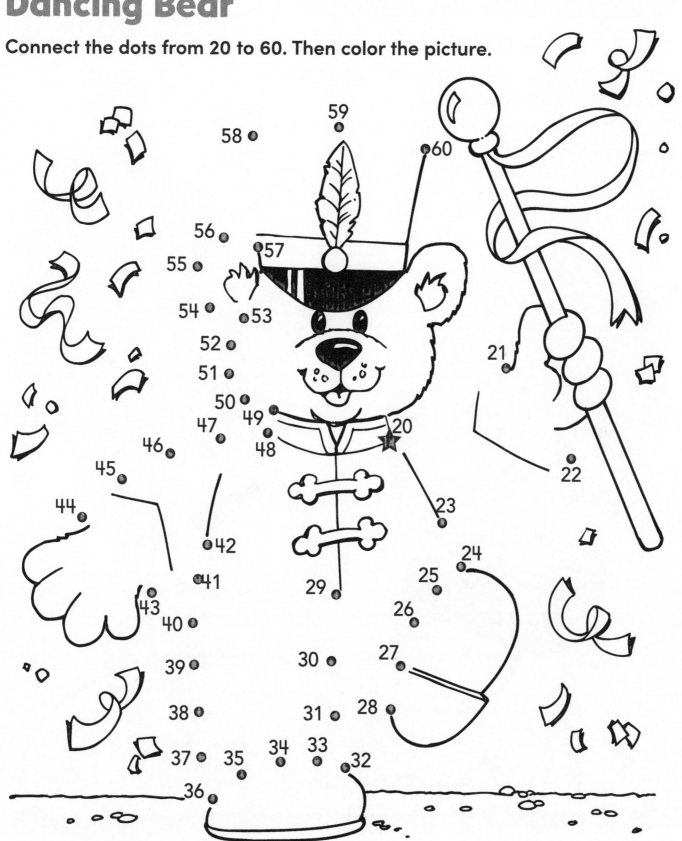

Snowflakes on Mittens

Estimate how many snowflakes are on each mitten.
For the first mitten, skip count by 2s to find out.
(You can circle groups of 2.)
For the second mitten, skip count by 5s to check your answer.
(You can circle groups of 5.)

⭐ Would snowflakes really wait for you to count them? Explain your answer.

Snail Mail

Get the snail to the mailbox. Count by 2s from 2 to 50.
Shade the boxes as you go.

51	33	15	7	42	13
50	11	39	44	45	40
25	48	46	52	38	19

13	29	35	47	3	1	36	49	43
53	18	20	31	45	7	17	34	5
16	14	49	22	5	23	3	51	32
37	41	12	7	24	26	28	30	55
54	10	11	27	31	1
9	21	8	6	4	**2**

SNAIL
125

Patterns of Five

Look at the number chart below. Starting with 1, count 5 squares. Color in the fifth space. Then count 5 more squares and color in the fifth square. Keep going until you reach 100.

Hundred's Chart

1	2	3	4	5	6	7	8	9	10
11	12	13	14	15	16	17	18	19	20
21	22	23	24	25	26	27	28	29	30
31	32	33	34	35	36	37	38	39	40
41	42	43	44	45	46	47	48	49	50
51	52	53	54	55	56	57	58	59	60
61	62	63	64	65	66	67	68	69	70
71	72	73	74	75	76	77	78	79	80
81	82	83	84	85	86	87	88	89	90
91	92	93	94	95	96	97	98	99	100

Tally marks can be arranged in groups of five, like this: ⅡⅡⅠ ⅡⅡⅠ ⅡⅡⅠ
Then you can count by fives.

Count how many girls you know. Draw tally marks in groups of fives.

Girls: _____ Boys: _____

Now count the total number. Write the totals here:

Girls: _____ Boys: _____

I Can Skip Count!

Skip count aloud by 10s. Write each number you say.

10, _____ , _____ , _____ , _____ ,

_____ , _____ , _____ , _____ , 100

Connect the dots. Start at 0. Count by 10s.

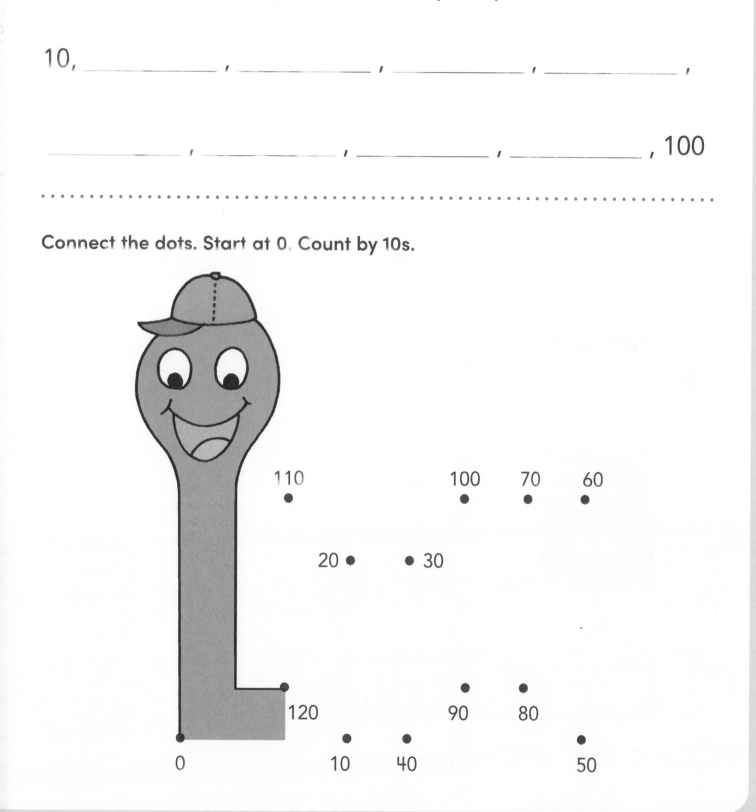

Sign Shape

Street signs come in different shapes. Use string to form the shapes below. Work with a partner. Answer the questions below about the shapes, too.

What shape is this sign? _____

How many sides does it have? _____

What shape is this sign? _____

How many sides does it have? _____

What shape is this sign? _____

How many sides does it have? _____

What shape is this sign? _____

How many sides does it have? _____

Bird Feeder Geometry

It's spring! The birds are coming back. Kwaku and his mother made two bird feeders.

What shapes can you find on their feeders? Write your ideas on the lines.

_____

_____

_____

Corners and Sides

Count the corners and sides on each shape.
Write the answers below each shape.

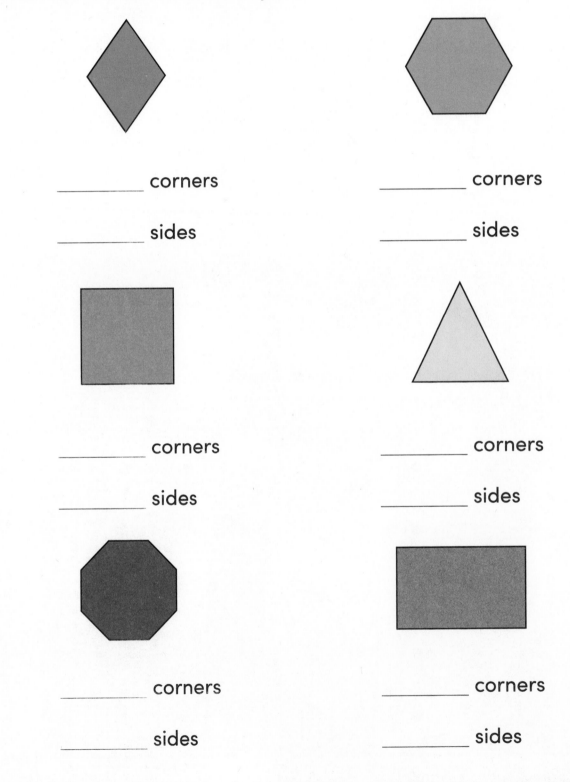

_____ corners

_____ sides

_____ corners

_____ sides

_____ corners

_____ sides

_____ corners

_____ sides

_____ corners

_____ sides

_____ corners

_____ sides

Shape Study

Look at the pictures below. Color those that show symmetry. (Hint: Imagine the pictures are folded on the dotted lines.)

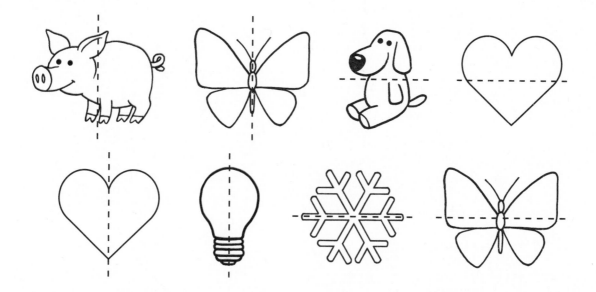

Complete the drawings below. Connect the dots to show the other half. (Hint: The pictures are symmetrical)

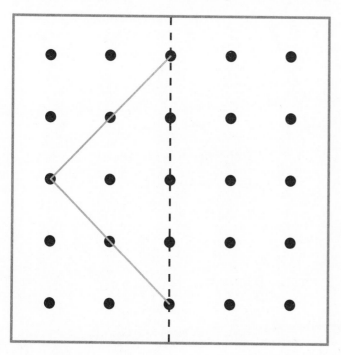 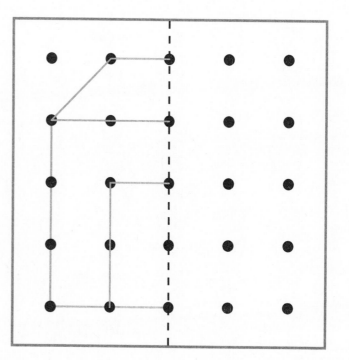

Equal Halves?

Color each shape that is divided into equal halves.

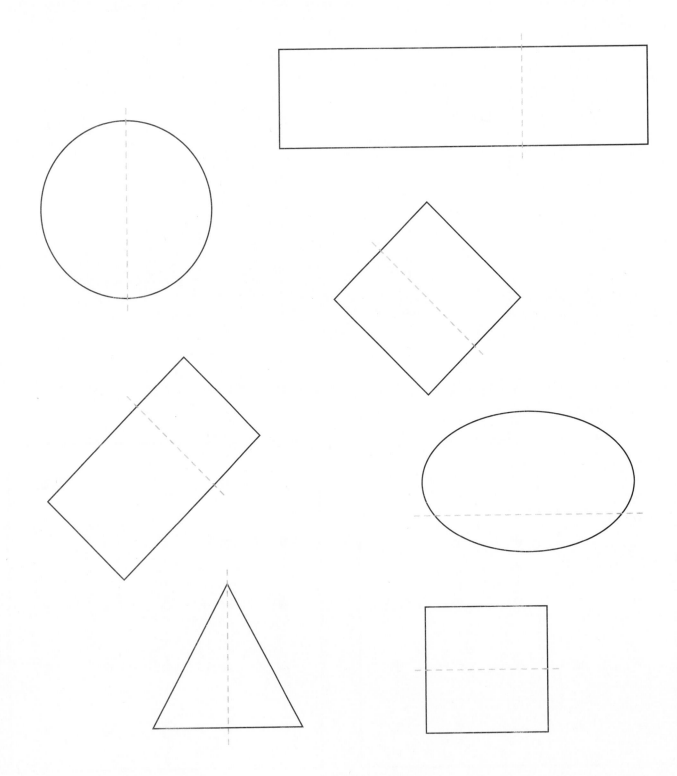

Give Us Symmetry!

Draw the other half of each shape.

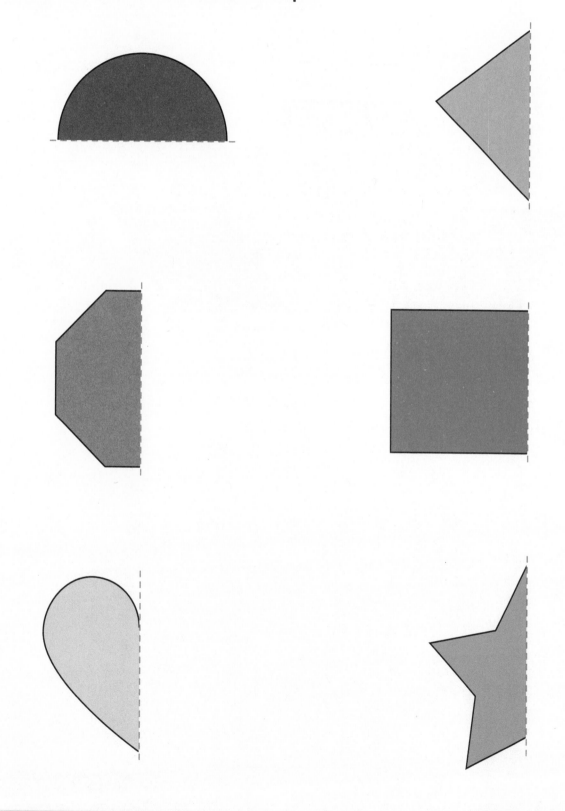

Pattern Block Design

How many total pieces are in this pattern block design?

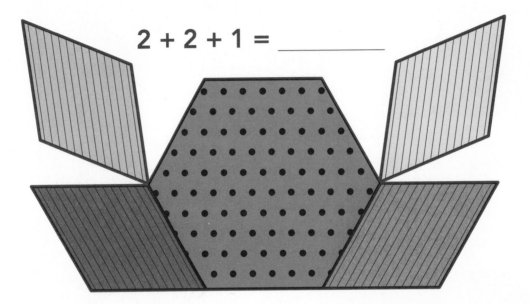

$$2 + 2 + 1 = \underline{\hspace{3cm}}$$

Now make your own design by drawing 5 pattern blocks. Connect the blocks to form a pattern different from the one above. You may want to use a block pattern more than once.

Write an equation to show how many of each shape you used.

Equation: _____

Time to Get Up!

Twenty animals were hibernating near Sleepy Pond.
5 of them woke up. Color 5 animals below.

How many are still sleeping? _____

A week later, 7 more woke up. Color 7 animals.

How many are still sleeping? _____

Money Matters

Alex asked his little brother Billy to trade piggy banks.

Alex's bank has these coins: Billy's bank has these coins:

Do you think this is a fair trade? _____

Test your answer:

Add up Alex's coins: _____

Add up Billy's coins: _____

Write the totals in this Greater Than/Less Than equation:

_____ > _____

Who has more money? _____

That's the Tooth!

Look at Felix Frog's teeth.

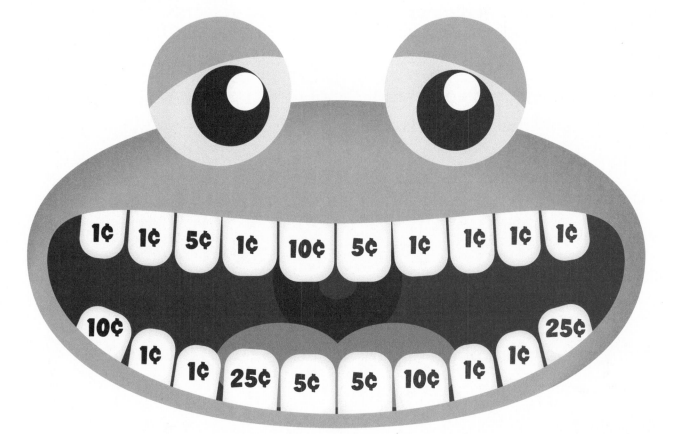

	How many teeth?	How much money in all?
1 How many 1¢?		cents
2 How many 5¢?		cents
3 How many 10¢?		cents
4 How many 25¢?		cents

Measuring Up

People didn't always measure with rulers.
Long ago, Egyptians and other people measured objects with body parts.
Try it!

A "digit" is the width of your middle finger
at the top joint where it bends.

How many digits long is:

a pair of scissors? _____

a math book? _____

a crayon? _____

A "palm" is the width of your palm.

How many palms long is:

a magazine? _____

your desk? _____

a ruler? _____

A "span" is the length from the tip of your pinkie
to the tip of your thumb when your hand is wide open.

How many spans long is:

a broom handle? _____

a table? _____

a door? _____

Penguin Family on Parade

The penguin family is part of the winter parade. They need to line up from shortest to tallest. Give them a hand! Use a ruler to measure each penguin. Label each penguin with its height. Then write the name of each penguin in size order, from smallest to tallest.

Paul
Height:

_____

inches

Peter
Height:

_____

inches

Patty
Height:

_____

inches

Petunia
Height:

_____

inches

Size Order:

_____ _____ _____ _____

(smallest)   (tallest)

Look and Learn

Look at each picture. Estimate how long you think it is. Then measure each picture with a ruler. Write the actual length in inches.

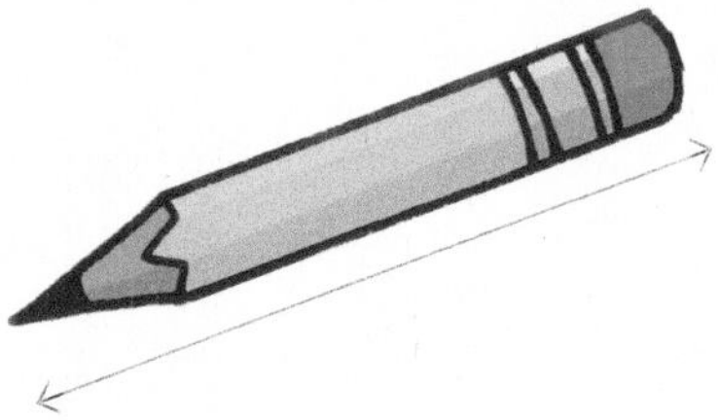

Estimate: _____ inches

Actual: _____ inches

Estimate: _____ inches

Actual: _____ inches

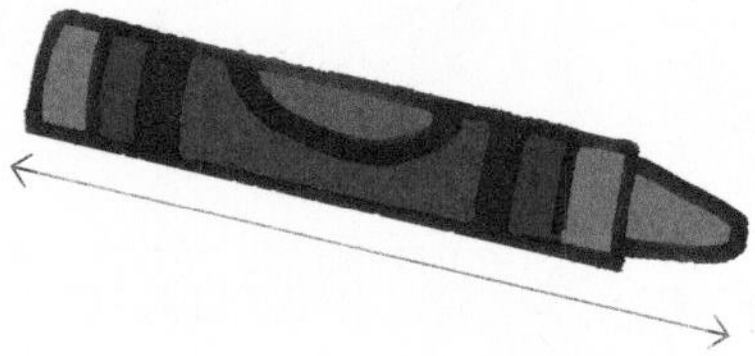

Estimate: _____ inches

Actual: _____ inches

Estimate: _____ inches

Actual: _____ inches

☆ Practice measuring other things in the room with a ruler.

Turn Up the Volume

How many quarts equal 1 gallon? Find out! Fill a quart container with water. Pour it into a gallon container. Keep doing it until the gallon is full. Color the correct number of quarts below.

Write the numeral on the line: **1 gallon = _____ quarts.**

Now try it with other containers

1 quart = _____ pints

1 pint = _____ cups

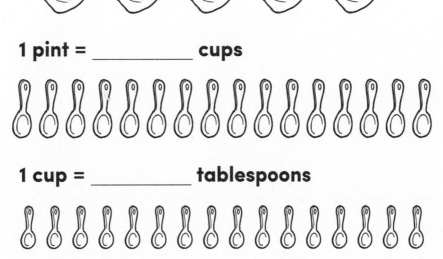

1 cup = _____ tablespoons

1 tablespoon = _____ teaspoons

Adding Sides

Use the inch side of a ruler and measure each side of each rectangle. Write the inches in the spaces below. Then add up all the sides to find the perimeter, or distance, around each rectangle.

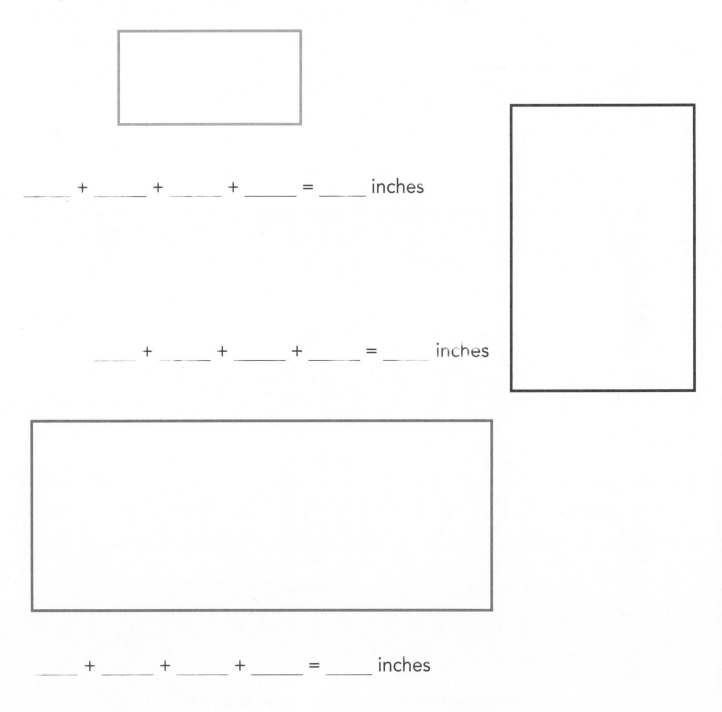

_____ + _____ + _____ + _____ = _____ inches

_____ + _____ + _____ + _____ = _____ inches

_____ + _____ + _____ + _____ = _____ inches

Centimeters

Things can be measured using centimeters. Get a ruler that measures in centimeters. Measure the pictures of the objects below.

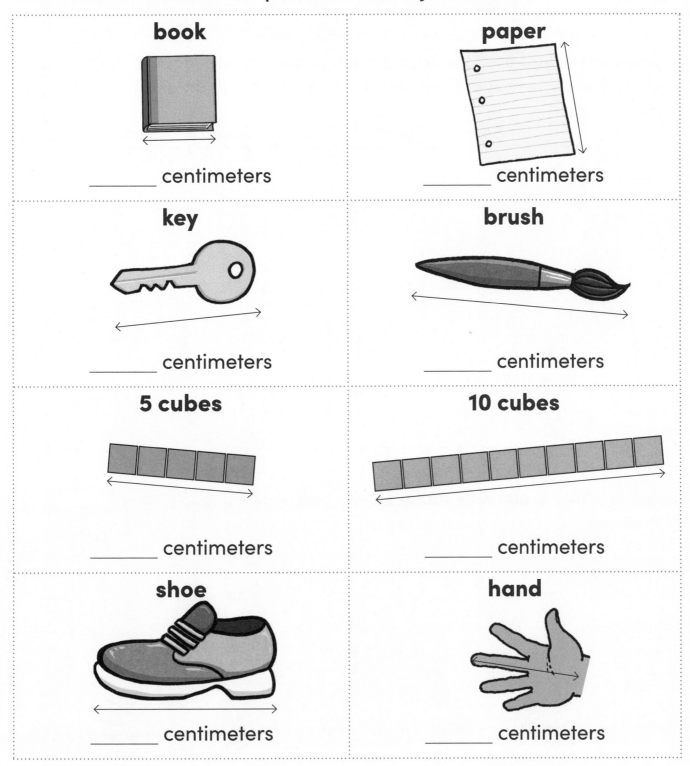

book

_____ centimeters

paper

_____ centimeters

key

_____ centimeters

brush

_____ centimeters

5 cubes

_____ centimeters

10 cubes

_____ centimeters

shoe

_____ centimeters

hand

_____ centimeters

Five Senses

We learn about the world by using our five senses.
The five senses are seeing, hearing, smelling, touching, and tasting.

**Look at the pictures on the left side of the graph. Think about which
of your senses you use to learn about it. Draw a check mark in the box
to show the senses used. (Hint: You might use more than one.)**

	See	Hear	Smell	Touch	Taste
🐔					
☀️					
🥛					
💐					
🥁					

Now graph how many senses you used for each object.

Rainbow Graph

Which color of the rainbow is your favorite?
Color in the box for your favorite color.
Have six friends color the boxes to show
their favorite colors, too.

Which color is liked the most? _____

Which color is liked the least? _____

Are any colors tied? _____

Which ones? _____

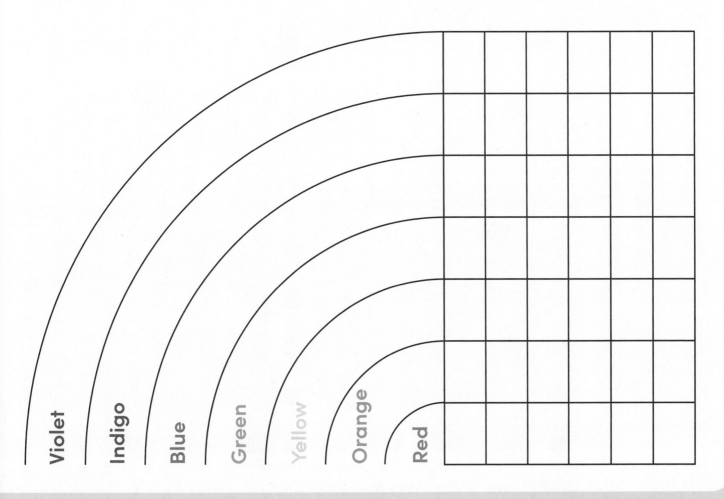

Fruits and Vegetables

Find the coordinates for each of the items in the grid.
The first one has been done for you.

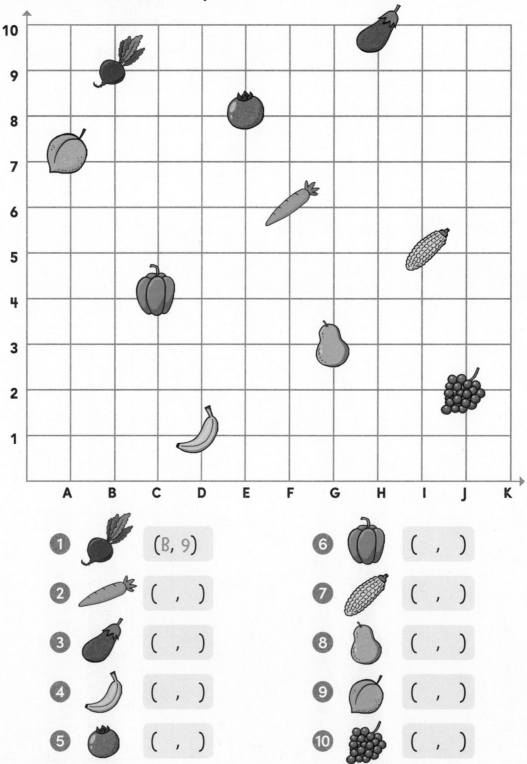

1. (B, 9)
2. (,)
3. (,)
4. (,)
5. (,)
6. (,)
7. (,)
8. (,)
9. (,)
10. (,)

Starry Night

Find each letter and number pair on the graph.
Draw a star for each. The first one has been done for you.

1 (F, 10) **4** (A, 4) **7** (I, 9) **10** (C, 1)

2 (G, 2) **5** (D, 8) **8** (K, 11) **11** (J, 5)

3 (B, 9) **6** (G, 6) **9** (D, 5) **12** (K, 2)

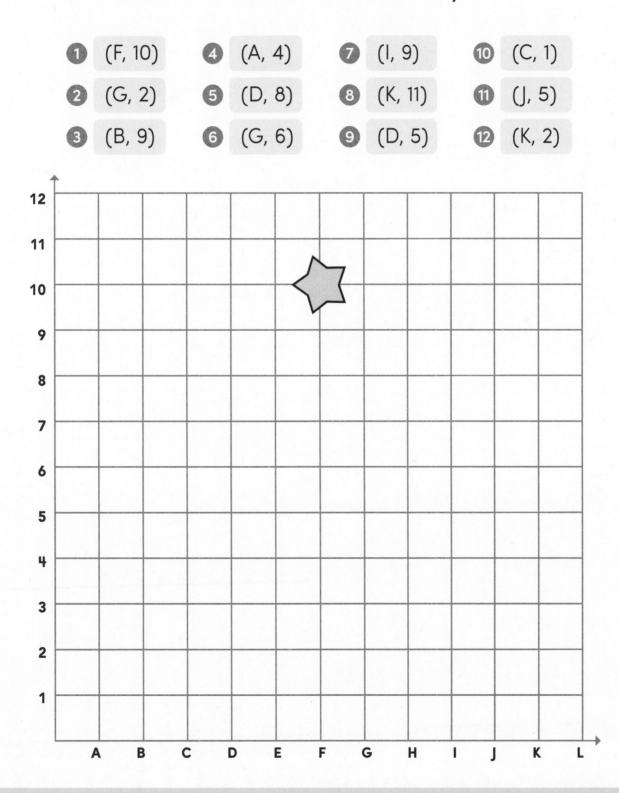

December Weather

In December, Mrs. Monroe's class drew the weather on a calendar.
Each kind of weather has a picture:

sunny   cloudy   rainy   snowy

Look at the calendar. Answer the questions below.

December

SUN.	MON.	TUES.	WED.	THURS.	FRI.	SAT.
	cloudy 1	cloudy 2	sunny 3	cloudy 4	rainy 5	snowy 6
rainy 7	snowy 8	snowy 9	sunny 10	sunny 11	cloudy 12	sunny 13
cloudy 14	sunny 15	sunny 16	snowy 17	sunny 18	cloudy 19	rainy 20
rainy 21	cloudy 22	sunny 23	sunny 24	rainy 25	snowy 26	sunny 27
snowy 28	cloudy 29	sunny 30	sunny 31			

How many sunny days did they have? _____

How many cloudy days did they have? _____

How many rainy days did they have? _____

How many snowy days did they have? _____

Which kind of weather did they have the most? _____

Fun With Fractions

The shapes below are split into parts, or fractions.
Color only the shapes that are split into
equal parts (equal fractions).

A **fraction** is a part of a whole.

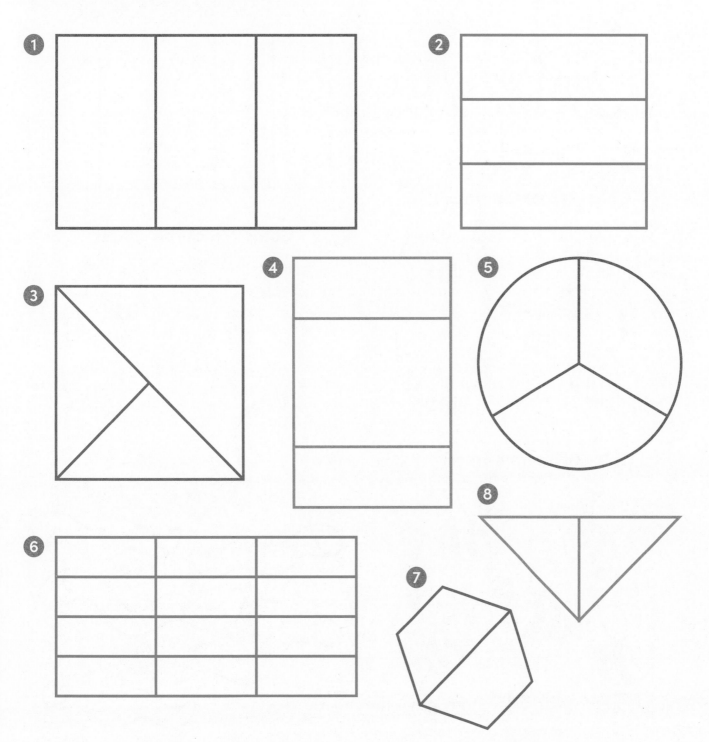

Parts to Color

Color 1/5 of the circle.

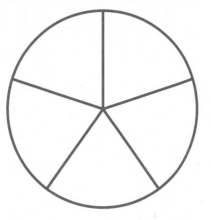

A **fraction** has two numbers. The top number will tell you how many parts to color. The bottom number tells you how many parts there are.

Color 4/5 of the rectangle.

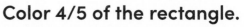

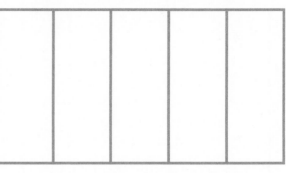

Color 3/5 of the ants.

Color 2/5 of the spiders.

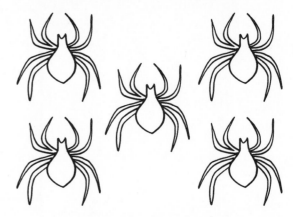

Color 0/5 of the bees.

Color 5/5 of the worms.

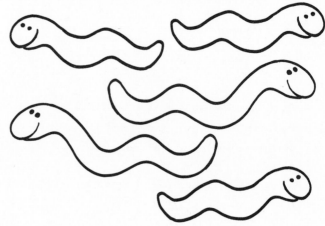

More Parts to Color

Color 1/8 of the circle.

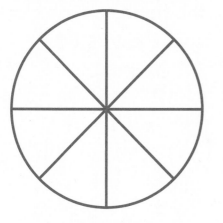

Color 6/8 of the rectangle.

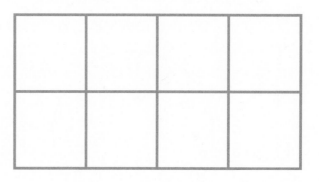

Color 4/8 of the suns.

Color 8/8 of the stars.

Color 2/8 of the moons.

Color 3/8 of the planets.

Clock Work

Draw the hands on the clock so it shows **2:00**.

Draw the hands on the clock so it shows **3:00**.

Draw the hands on the clock so it shows **4:00**.

Draw the hands on the clock so it shows **5:00**.

What do you do at 2:00 in the afternoon?
Write about it on the lines below.

_____

_____

More Clock Work

Draw the hands on the clock so it shows **3:00**.

Draw the hands on the clock so it shows **6:00**.

Draw the hands on the clock so it shows **9:00**.

Draw the hands on the clock so it shows **12:00**.

What do you do at 3:00 in the afternoon?
Write about it on the lines below.

_____

_____

Even More Clock Work

Draw the hands on the clock so it shows **4:00**.

Draw the hands on the clock so it shows **4:30**.

What do you do at 4:00 in the afternoon? Write about it on the line below.

_____

Draw the hands on the clock so it shows **6:00**.

Draw the hands on the clock so it shows **6:30**.

What do you do at 6:00 in the evening? Write about it on the line below.

_____

About Time

Why do we need to know how to tell time? List your ideas below.

_____

_____

_____

_____

How long is a minute?

Think about how much you can do in one minute.
Write your estimates in the Prediction column.
Then time yourself. Write the actual number
in the Result column.

Prediction: In one minute I can...	Result
jump rope _____ times.	
write the numbers 1 to _____.	
say the names of _____ animals.	

Balloon Clocks

Read each balloon clock. Then draw a line to connect it with the matching time.

| 6:30 | 8:40 | 7:15 | 3:20 |

| 5:00 | 2:05 | 4:50 | 1:45 |

ANSWER KEY

READING COMPREHENSION

Page 12
1. a good reader 2. looks at the picture 3. the title 4. the words

Page 13
Main idea: Trucks do important work.

Page 14
Main idea: Acrobats can do great things.

Page 15
KATE: Names have special meanings.
Casey means brave.
George means farmer.
Sarah means princess.

Page 16

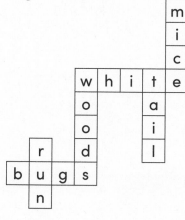

Page 17

1. in reading class 2. camping

Page 18
Kelly packed pajamas, shirt, shorts, toothbrush, toothpaste, hairbrush, swimsuit, pillow, storybooks, sunglasses.
Compound words: grandmother, suitcase, toothbrush, toothpaste, hairbrush, swimsuit, storybooks, sunglasses

Page 19
1. Texas 2. oil 3. president
4. wife 5. Jenna
His cat's name was INDIA

Page 20
Fantasy: ketchup bottles and a watermelon bowling, a talking milk jug, dancing bananas, chicken wings that can fly all by themselves, laughing soup cans, dancing carrots

Page 21
Facts: Clouds float in the sky. Clouds are made of tiny drops of water. Fog is a cloud on the ground. (All others are fantasy.)

Page 22
Fantasy: pig, goat and sheep, horses, pizza and sandwiches, mouse, golden eggs
(The others are real.)

Page 23
5, 4, 3, 1, 2
Tara bought pencils, scissors, glue and crayons.

Page 24
6, 4, 2; 3, 1, 5
LEARN TO DIVE

Page 25
1. Each star should be outlined in blue and colored red inside.
2. One moon should be yellow and one orange.
3. A face should be drawn on each sun.
4. 3 5. 2 6. 4 7. 3 + 2 + 4 = 9
8. stars and moon

Page 26

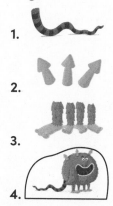

Page 27
The pictures that do not belong are pumpkin, snowman, frog, and skates. (The other pictures should be colored.)
2. hot, cold 3. yellow

Page 28
IT WAS A FLYING CARPET.
No

Page 29
1. true 2. false 3. false
4. true 5. true

Page 30
Pictures should include everything described in the sentences.

Page 31
The following should have been added to the picture: black clouds, lightning striking the tallest tree, the word "Moo" in a bubble above a cow, rain, a mud puddle by the barn door, hay blowing out of the barn window

Page 32
1. penguin 2. octopus
3. grandmother 4. ant

Page 33
1. head lice
2. The children had itchy scalps.
3. 9 4. She got head lice, too.

Page 34

Page 35

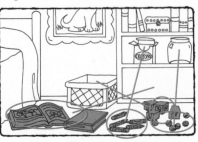

The hamburger does not belong.

Page 36
Sadie's Shoe Store: sandals, boots, sneakers
Movie Town Cinema: tickets, popcorn, big screen, candy
Pepe's Mexican Food: tacos, burritos, beans, peppers
Garden Shop: tulip bulbs, fertilizer, shovel, soil

Page 37
Answers will vary.

Page 38

Page 39

He knew he had to do the right thing.

Page 40
FAST FOOD, FLOWER BED

Page 41

Same: They are in the first grade.

Page 42
Juan's mother: She is a captain. She works on a ship. She is in the Navy.
Ann's mother: She is a pilot. She is in the Air Force. She flies a jet. (The other sentences apply to both mothers.)

Page 43

1.
2.
3.

Page 44
1. an arm like paddle
2. not dangerous 3. slap at
4. lose 5. hide in the ground

Page 45
1. little furry animals 2. tunnels
3. rooms 4. pests

Page 46
1. Sandy used lanterns at night because the cabin had no electricity.
2. Sandy and Austin bathed in a stream because the cabin had no running water.
3. Sandy felt better about missing Kendra because she talked to her on the cell phone.
4. Sandy's dad could not call his office because the cell phone was dead.

Page 47
1. Wanda and Carl got tangled up when they danced.
2. They were tied in a knot so they got married.

Page 48
1. C 2. B 3. D 4. F 5. A 6. E

Page 49
Pictures should show a crown on Margie's arm, a shoe on her head, different colors on each fingernail, a red nose, a fork in her hair, and a purple belt around her knees.
1. the way she dresses
2. He wears his clothes backward.

Page 50
1. happy 2. worried 3. silly
4. sad 5. scared 6. surprised

Page 51
Green: helpful, does the right thing
Red: forgets to do chores, could get Ty in trouble
Yellow: make-believe characters

Page 52
Picture: rainbow 1. appear
2. gold Picture: airplane
3. high 4. again 5. bee

Page 53
2. Don't be greedy. Be happy with what you have.
Color: dog, meat, bridge

Page 54

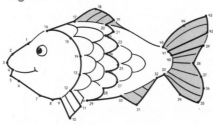

1. sharing 2. Marcus Pfister

GRAMMAR

Page 102
1. The 2. The 3. The 4. The
5. The 6. The
Circle sentence 2 and 6.

Page 103
1. The cat sat. 2. The dog sat.
3. I see the cat. 4. I can see.

Page 104
1. The 2. Jon 3. Ants
4. My 5. I 6. We

Page 105
1. I see Jan.
2. We see Dan.
3. I go with Jan.
4. I go with Dan and Jan.
1. school. 2. school.

Page 106
1. Dan is in the cab.
2. The cat is in the cab.
3. Mom is in the cab.
4. We see Dan and Mom.
1. van. 2. red.

Page 107
1. The cat is on the mat.
2. The rat sees the cat.
3. The cat and rat sit.
4. The rat is on the mat.
5. The rat can hop.

Page 108
1. I like to hop.
2. I can hop to Mom.
3. Pam and I like to hop.
4. Mom and I can hop.
Answers will vary.

Page 109
1—4. Write I on the lines.
Answers will vary.

Page 110
1. I sit on a mat.
2. I see the van.
3. I like to nap.
4. Pam and I like cats.
5. I like jam.
6. I like the park.

Page 111
1. Pam 2. Dan
3. The cat 4. The van

1. Jon is hot.

2. The hat is on top.

3. The man sat.

Page 112
1. Bill paints.
2. Tom likes to read.
3. Pat plants flowers.
4. Leon cooks.
5. Answers will vary.

Page 113
1. The cat sits on a mat.
2. I see Mom.
3. Ben can hop.
4. Pam and Dan like jam.
5. I like my hat.
6. Dina rides a bike.

Page 114
1. I 2. We 3. Pam 4. We
1. I like dots.
2. We like hats.
3. Pam likes dots.
4. We like hats with dots.

Page 115
1. I like cats.
2. I see a man.
3. We go to school.

Page 116
1. I see red dots.
2. The cat is fat.
3. Ben likes jam.
4. Dan is in a big van.
5. We like the hat.
6. Jada rides a bike.

Page 117
1. ? 2. ? 3. ? 4. ? ;
1. Answers will vary.
2. Answers will vary.

Page 118
1. Who hid the cat ?
2. Can the cat see the rat ?
4. Can the van go ?
1. Can we sit in the van?
2. Can Dan nap in the van?

Page 119
1. Who hid my hat?
2. Did the hat have dots?
3. Can you see the hat?
4. Did Jan like my hat?
5. Dan has the hat?

Page 120
1. pig 2. pan
3. Pam 4. you, hill

1. The sun is hot.
2. Sam ran and ran.
3. Is the cat fat?

Page 121
1. Al, van 2. cat, mat
3. Pat, hill 4. Dan, Jan
Pictures and sentences will vary.

Page 122
1. cat 2. rat 3. map
4. van 5. fan

Page 123
1. Hill Park 2. Don 3. Pam
4. Frog Lake
Answers will vary.

Page 124
1. Pam 2. Ron 3. Ant Hill
4. Bat Lake
1. Spot 2. Hill Street

Page 125
1. Don 2. Pig Hill 3. Jan
4. Jam Street 5. Ham Lake

Page 126
1. clucks 2. ran 3. hid 4. naps
1. run 2. see

Page 127
1. see 2. sits 3. mops
4. run 5. hops

Page 128
1. sit 2. ran 3. mop
4. digs 5. hops

Page 129
1. big 2. fast 3. bad 4. fat
1. big 2. little

Page 130
1. little, fast 2. hot, big

1. It is fat.
2. They are little.

Page 131
1. silly 2. black 3. green
4. fast 5. big 6. gray

Page 132
1. I see the basket .
2. The cat is in the basket .
3. Hats can go in it .
4. The sock can go in it .
1. I can fill the basket.
3. We can clean.
5. He jogs on Mondays.
6. She helps her father cook.

Page 133
1. She has a mop.
2. The dog is on top.
3. Dan gets the hats.
4. Ron can clean spots.
1. Put it in the pot .

Page 134
1. You can get it.
2. The hat is in the basket.
3. We can fill the basket.
4. The basket is big.
5. A cat cannot go in it.
6. I put the toys in the basket.

Page 135
1. Help ! The cat is on top !
2. Get the cat !
3. This cat is bad !
4. Uh-oh ! The cat is wet !
1. Oh my! Get the dog!
2. Oh! The dog runs!

Page 136
1. Run to the show!
2. Oh my, I'm very late!
3. What a great show!
4. Watch out, the floor is wet!
5. Wow, we had lots of fun!

Page 137
1. Yes! The cow can kick!
2. That rat runs fast!
3. The pot is hot!
4. That cat is bad!
5. Oh no! A frog is in my house!

Page 138

1. Let's go
2. I am a kid
3. Why doesn't the clock work
4. Do you have a hat
5. This game is fun
6. I play soccer
7. What's your name
8. The beach is great
9. My name is Paul

Page 139

1. hats 2. girls
3. eggs 4. cats
1. mugs 2. hands

Page 140

1. Jan has her mittens.
2. Jan runs with her dogs.
3. She will run up hills.
4. The dogs can jump.
1. cats 2. socks

Page 141

1. hands 2. dogs 3. frogs
4. pots 5. ants 6. kittens

Page 142

1. sits 2. digs 3. sees 4. naps
1. sees 2. run

Page 143

1. play 2. dance 3. talk 4. run

Page 144

1. sits 2. hops 3. ran
4. naps 5. digs 6. jumps

Page 145

1. We, school 2. girl
3. ball 4. friends
Person: girl
Place: school
Animal: rabbit
Thing: ball

Page 146

1. Run and kick in the (park.)
2. Kick with a (foot.)
3. Kick the (ball.)
4. The (girl) will run.
5. Kick into the (net.)

Page 147

1. park 2. ball 3. net
4. girl 5. friend

Page 148

1. The king is sad.
2. Tell the king to come.
3. Let's bake him a cake.
4. Let's eat the cake.
The king eats.

Page 149

1. This bear likes snow.
2. The water is cold.
3. The bear runs fast.
4. Two bears play.

Page 150

1. Pam will bake a cake.
2. The king has a duck.
3. The king will eat cake.
4. Pam will see the king.
5. The duck is in the lake.
6. Ramon will help Pam bake.

Page 151

circle: What, See, Night,
The, Light, Moon,
See, Many, Stars,
The, Sun, Moon
Answers will vary.

Page 152

1. look, stars
2. the, moon, shines, night
3. we, see, planets
4. many, moons, shine
5. night, day
1. The Sun in the Sky
2. See the Stars! .

Page 153

1. Where Is the Sun?
2. Day and Night
3. The Big, Bad Wolf
4. Many Cats to See
5. How Many Pigs?
6. Ant and Cricket Play

Page 154

1. pot 2. top 3. pan 4. Jim

1. The pot is hot.
2. See the pan?
3. Jim is fast.

Page 155

1. Jan, van 2. van, hill
3. van 4. Dan, Jan
Answers will vary.

Page 156

1. pans 2. Jim 3. rat
4. cat 5. cat 6. puppy

Page 157

1. is 2. was 3. were 4. are
1. now 2. in the past 3. now

Page 158

1. are, now 2. is, now
3. was, past 4. is, now
5. were, past

Page 159

1. was 2. are 3. are 4. were
5. is 6. is

Page 160
1. Raul 2. Ms. Chin
3. Sue 4. Mr. Poh

Page 161
1. The 2. They
3. The, Nosey 4. Nosey
1. Dan and Pam like the play.
Names a special person,
place, animal, or thing.
2. They will read it to Jim.
First word in a sentence.

Page 162
1. I 2. Ron 3. Gruff 4. A
5. Nosey

WRITING

Page 164

The	For	That	with	know	but
here	on	When	Have	next	we
as	after	good	Make	there	see
Go	Look	Are	Could	is	why
This	who	said	in	come	them
Has	Name	Before	Her	Where	The

Page 165
1. The mouse 2. He finds
3. He eats 4. Then he
5. Oh no 6. The mouse

Page 166
1. We read 2. Then we
3. My bed 4. My cat
5. The sky 6. My eyes

Page 167
1. My dog 2. She must
3. Maybe she
4. Sometimes she 5. I think

Page 168
Check that a period has
been added to the end of
each sentence.

Page 169
Check that a period has
been added to the end of
each sentence.

Page 170
1. Frogs and toads lay eggs.
2. The eggs are in the water.
3. Tadpoles hatch from the eggs.
4. The tadpoles grow legs.
5. The tadpoles lose their tails.

Page 171
1. Tadpoles become frogs
   or toads.
2. Frogs live near water.
3. Toads mostly live on dry land.
4. Frogs have wet skin.
5. Toads have bumpy skin.

Page 172
The following sentences
should be colored green:
This is a rug.
The rug has stripes.
Some stripes are green.
Some stripes are yellow.
The rug has a fringe.
The fringe is purple and blue.
The rug is colorful.
The rest are not sentences
and should be yellow.

Page 173

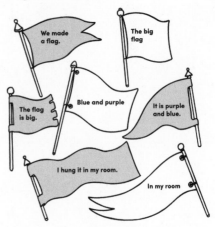

Page 174
Four fish are swimming.
We have one shovel.

Page 175
1. A jaguar is hiding.
2. Some butterflies are blue.
3. Frogs jump in the water.
4. Green snakes hang from trees.
5. The trees grow very tall.

Page 176
The snakes on the left side of the
page should have been colored.

Page 177
1. The blue snakes
2. The yellow snake
3. The green snake
4. The brown snake
5. The red snake
6. The purple snake
7. The black snake
8. The orange snake

Page 178
Sentences will vary.

Page 179
Sentences will vary.

Page 180
Sentences will vary.

Page 181
Sentences will vary.

Page 182
The bones on the right side of the page should have been colored.

Page 183
1. is jumping.
2. is playing.
3. is eating.
4. is sleeping.

Page 184
Sentences will vary.

Page 185
Sentences will vary.

Page 186
Sentences will vary.

Page 187
Sentences will vary.

Page 188
Drawings will vary.

Page 189
1. long ago 2. yesterday
3. in winter 4. today
5. in the fall 6. last night
7. all day 8. at noon
9. yesterday
10. on Thanksgiving Day
11. this morning 12. Tomorrow

Page 190
Sentences will vary.

Page 191
Sentences will vary.

Page 192
Answers will vary.

Page 193
Sentences will vary.

Page 194
Sentences will vary.

Page 195
Sentences will vary.

Page 196
blanket, bat, cracker, ball

Page 197
sweet, red, smooth
bumpy, salty, crunchy
gray, squeaky, furry

Page 198
Lollipop: hard, shiny, sticky
Chick: soft, fluffy, fuzzy
Answers will vary.

Page 199
Adjectives will vary.

Page 200
Sentences will vary.

Page 201
Sentences will vary.

Page 202
Sentences will vary.

Page 203
Sentences will vary.

Page 204
Sentences will vary.

Page 205
My Space Friend, A Big Beak
The Big Win, A Knight's Tale

Page 206
Stories will vary.

Page 207
Sentences will vary.

Page 208
Sentences and pictures will vary.

MAPS

Page 210
climber, seesaw, slide, umbrella, bench

Page 211
1. Answers will vary but should show an understanding that the picture and map represent the same area.
2. Answers will vary but should indicate that the picture is an actual image of the playground taken from above whereas the map is a drawing that shows the location of things in the playground.
3. climber, seesaw, slide, umbrella, bench

Page 212
1. rug
2. window

Page 213
Your child should have drawn a map of his or her bedroom.

Page 214
1. Earth
2. round
3. water

Page 215
1. a model of Earth
2. land and water
3. into two equal parts

Pages 216
True statements are 1 and 3.

Pages 217
North and South America should be green, the Atlantic Ocean and parts of the Pacific Ocean should be blue, Europe, Africa, Asia, Australia, and Antarctica should be gray, the Arctic, Indian, and Southern Oceans and part of the Pacific Ocean should be light blue.

Page 218
True statements are 2 and 3.

Page 219
1. school
2. flower shop
3. Tanya's Neighborhood
4. Parker School Playground

Page 220
1. far
2. far
3. near

Page 221
1. school
2. library
3. firehouse
4. park
5. offices
6. church

Page 222
1. right
2. left
3. left

Page 223
1. Your child should put an X on red elephant.
2. Your child should circle camel.

Page 224
1. north
2. north
3. south

Page 225
1. south
2. south
3. north

Page 226
Symbols will vary but should represent pictures shown and should include a label.

Page 227
1. Swing
2. Bench
3. 4

Pages 228
1. Your child should draw an X on the blue oval representing water.
2. Your child should draw a circle around the rock shapes at the upper right-hand corner of the lake.
3. Your child should draw a check mark on the trees at the upper left-hand corner of the lake.

Pages 229
Your child should first draw the picnic table, tent, and logs on the map. Maps will vary but may include symbols for things such as a hiking trail or fishing dock.

Page 230
1. Route should follow Green Road south, Library Way west, Park Road north, and then School Street east.
2. Route should follow Green Road south, Library Way east, Park Road north, and the School Street west.

Page 231
1. There should be a check mark on the school symbol. Its address is 19 School Street.
2. There should be a circle around the library symbol. Its address is 32 Library Way.
3. There should be a star on the symbol for Jason's house. Its address is 4 Green Road.

Page 233
Your child should trace a route that starts at the word "start" on the map near the west wall, goes south then east to Blue Lake, east across the bridge and onto the island then across the bridge on the other side of the island, up the hill and east to a big rock, south to end at the old tree.

Page 234
1. Your child should add symbols to the map and map key that represent different places on the island. Your child should label the symbols in the map key.

Page 235
1. There should be a circle around the Dolphin Show.
2. There should be a check mark on the Alligator Band.
3. There should be a star on the Octopus Show.
4. There should be a line under the Seal Show.
5. There should be an X on the Penguin Show

Page 236
1. Both a mountain and a hill are higher than the land around them.
2. A mountain is much higher than a hill.

Page 237
1. mountain
2. lake
3. river

Page 238
1. There should be a star on the mountain in the upper right-hand corner of the map.
2. hill; There should be a check mark on the hills in the upper half of the map.
3. There should be an X on the river that flows from the lake on the map.
4. water

Page 239
Maps will vary but should include a title on the line provided, symbols on the map, and a map key that explains what the symbols on the map are.

Page 240
1. North America, South America, Europe, Asia, Africa, Australia, Antarctica
2. Australia
3. Asia

Page 241
1. There are two Pacific Ocean labels. **2.** north **3.** Australia
4. Atlantic Ocean

Page 242
1. Canada
2. south
3. Atlantic Ocean
4. Pacific Ocean

Page 245
1. There should be a check on Nevada.
2. There should be stars on California, Oregon, Utah, Arizona, and Idaho.
3. five
4. north
5. west
6. east

Page 246
1. There should be a circle around Sacramento.
2. There should be a check mark on Providence.
3. There should be a star on the boundary line between California and Mexico.

Page 247
1. south
2. west
3. Connecticut
4. Arizona
5. east

Page 249
1. south
2. Independence Ave.
3. west to east
4. Answers will vary.

Page 250
1. offices **2.** left
3. east and south

Page 251
True statements are 2 and 3.

Page 252
1. south
2. lake
3. border
4. symbol
5. mountain
6. route
Secret Words: United States

SCIENCE

Page 256
2. lamb
3. tadpole
4. duckling
5. fawn
6. cub
7. calf
8. piglet
9. chick
10. puppy

Page 257–261
Investigation 1: Results will vary. Your child may notice that taking small, "waddling" steps helps to keep the egg on the feet.
Investigation 2: Colors will vary. Bird 1: Color(s) chosen should stand out against the habitat shown.
Bird 2: Color(s) chosen should blend in with the habitat.

Page 262

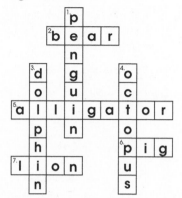

Page 263–267
Investigation 1: Signs of life will vary.
Investigation 2: Changes will vary depending on the animal chosen. Your child should consider the needs of the animal and suggest changes to accommodate it in your community park.

Page 268

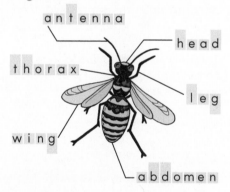

Page 269–273
Investigation 1: The more colors of glitter your child uses, the easier it will be to see how widely the pollen has spread.
Investigation 2: Your child may decide to simply draw a flower on white paper or make a more complicated one using materials such as construction paper, pipe cleaners, and so on.

Page 274–275

Is it a **butterfly**? Or is it a **moth**?

Both kinds of insects are colorful. Most butterflies have bright colors. Moths have pale colors.

Butterflies and moths need to keep warm. But they keep warm in different ways. A butterfly warms itself in the sun. A moth warms up by moving its wings.

Both insects fly. Butterflies fly in the day. But moths fly at night.

1. moths and butterflies
Sample answer: The article is about how moths and butterflies are the same and different.
2. It flaps its wings.
Sample answer: It says in paragraph 3 that a moth warms up by moving its wings.
3. Answers will vary. Check that students' responses are different from what they underlined in the article.

Pages 276–277

Auks and **hawks** are birds. Like all birds, both lay eggs. Both fly and hunt.

In other ways, auks and hawks are different. Auks are black and white. Hawks come in many colors.

Auks have short legs with webbed feet. Hawks have long, strong legs. They have sharp claws.

Auks eat fish and other sea life. Hawks eat small land animals, snakes, and insects.

1. hawks and auks
Sample answer: The article compares and contrasts two kinds of birds—auks and hawks.
2. Both lay eggs.
Sample answer: The article says this in the first paragraph.
3. Sample answers: The auk is on the top. I can see its webbed feet. The hawk is on the bottom. I can see its sharp claws.

Page 278

Brachiosaurus, Tyrannosaurus rex, Stegosaurus, Triceratops, Trachodon; extinct

Page 279

1. many foods we eat come from plants.
2. fruits.
3. fruits and grains.

Pages 280–281

Thumbs are special fingers.

All your fingers can move in and out. All can move from side to side. All can bend and wiggle. All can move in a circle. But only a thumb can touch every other fingertip. No other fingers can meet like this. Try it. Your thumbs help you grab and hold things. Can you pick up a penny without using your thumb?

1. touch every other fingertip
Sample answer: It says in the sixth sentence that only thumbs can do this.
2. pick things up
Sample answer: The article says that this is something thumbs help you do.
3. Sample answer: It was really hard to grab the penny without using my thumb.

Pages 282–283

Almost anything can cause a sneeze. You might breathe in some dust, cold air, or even pepper. It tickles the inside of your nose. So you need to clear it out.

Your brain gets the message. It signals some muscles to get ready to help. When they do, you suddenly feel the results. Your eyes close tight. Your mouth opens, and you sneeze: AHHH…CHOO! The tickle is gone.

1. It sends messages to muscles that can help. Sample answer: It says this at the beginning of the second paragraph.
2. You feel ticklish all over. Sample answer: I picked this because I read the other two choices in the article.
3. Sample answer: Sneezing gets rid of a tickle inside my nose.

Page 284
1. spring
2. winter
3. fall
4. summer
5. spring
6. winter
7. fall
8. summer
Pattern should show flower, snowflake, leaf, sun

Pages 285–289
Investigation 1: Observations will vary depending on the season.
Investigation 2: Answers will vary depending on the season but children should be able to determine whether the days are getting shorter or longer based on the change in sunrise and sunset times over a two-week period.

Pages 290–291

A **flood** happens when water

spills over. What causes a flood?

> Snow melts off mountains in the spring.
>
> It turns into water.
>
> The water runs downhill.
>
> It flows into rivers.
>
> Rainstorms add more water to rivers.
>
> Rivers can't hold all that extra water.

So they **overflow**.

The water covers everything nearby.

Floods soak fields, roads, and towns.

1. spill over Sample answer: The article says that when rivers can't hold extra water, they overflow. And the first sentence says that a flood happens when water spills over.
2. fields and towns Sample answer: The article says that melting snow and rain can cause floods. Floods happen to fields and towns.
3. Sample answer: In spring, it gets warmer and that would make snow melt and turn into water.

Page 292
2. hail
3. tornado
4. rain
5. snow
6. sunshine

Pages 293–297
Investigation 1: Blowing on the stars and triangles will work best to turn the Spin Wheel. The more power you use to blow, the faster it will push the pinwheel.
Investigation 2: Responses will vary.

Page 298

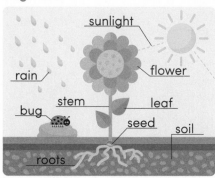

Shape code: botanist

Page 299
Earth, Saturn, Mars, Mercury, Uranus, Venus, Jupiter, Neptune

Page 300
1. It sent them to Earth.
2. red.
3. not wet.

MATH

Page 302

Page 303
1 + 2 = 3, 2 + 3 = 5, 7 + 3 = 10;
3 + 4 = 7, 1 + 0 = 1, 3 + 2 = 5;
1 + 1 = 2, 4 + 4 = 8; 1 + 3 = 4;
The ladybug with 10 spots should be colored red. The ladybug with 1 spot should be colored blue.

Page 304
Check that the correct number of flowers have been drawn.
7: needs 3
10: needs 5
4: needs 1
6: needs 2
9: needs 5
5: needs 3
8: needs 4
3: needs 2
Color the bows with the numbers 4, 6, 8, and 10 yellow. Color the bows with 3, 5, 7, and 9 purple.

Page 305

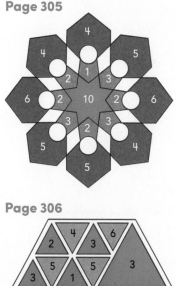

Page 306

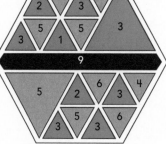

Page 307
2, 3, 2; 2, 3, 1

Pages 308–309
1. $10 - 3 = 7$
2. $6 - 4 = 2$
3. $10 - 1 = 9$
4. $8 - 7 = 1$
5. $4 - 1 = 3$
6. $10 - 4 = 6$
7. $10 - 6 = 4$
8. $10 - 8 = 2$
9. $7 - 4 = 3$

Page 310

Page 311

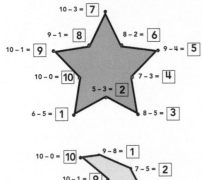

Page 312
4, 3, 2; 10, 1, 7; 6, 8, 5

Page 313

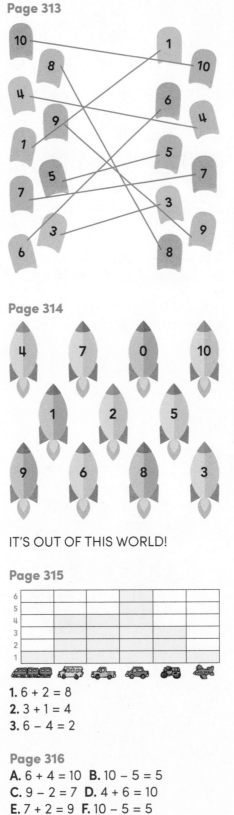

Page 314

IT'S OUT OF THIS WORLD!

Page 315

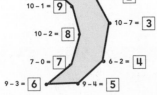
1. $6 + 2 = 8$
2. $3 + 1 = 4$
3. $6 - 4 = 2$

Page 316
A. $6 + 4 = 10$ B. $10 - 5 = 5$
C. $9 - 2 = 7$ D. $4 + 6 = 10$
E. $7 + 2 = 9$ F. $10 - 5 = 5$
G. $4 + 6 = 10$ H. $2 + 3 = 5$
I. $6 - 4 = 2$ J. $10 - 3 = 7$

Page 317
A. $7 + 3 = 10$
B. $7 - 4 = 3$
C. $10 - 6 = 4$
D. $8 - 2 = 6$
E. $5 + 4 = 9$

Page 318

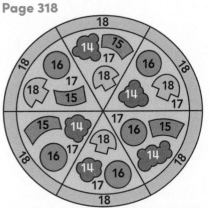

Page 319

7 leaps

Page 320

Page 321

6 + 2 = 8, 4 + 3 = 7, 2 + 1 = 3,
4 + 1 = 5, 11 + 3 = 14, 8 + 2 = 10,
7 + 5 = 12, 9 + 2 = 11, 6 + 3 = 9,
11 + 4 = 15, 5 + 13 = 18, 9 + 4 = 13;
A PIANO

Page 322

2	4	6
3	1	4
5	5	**10**

4	1	5
7	3	10
11	4	**15**

6	7	13
2	1	3
8	8	**16**

5	6	11
4	3	7
9	9	**18**

4	7	11
3	3	6
7	10	**17**

Page 323

8, 8; 4, 4; 6, 6; 8, 8; 2, 2; 3, 3;
9, 9; 1, 1; 5, 5; 7, 7; even

Page 324

7 + 7 = 14, 5 + 5 = 10, 8 + 8 = 16,
6 + 6 = 12;
9 + 9 = 18, 3 + 3 = 6, 2 + 2 = 4;
4 + 4 = 8

Page 325

4, 6, 10, 9, 7;
2, 5, 8, 3, 1;
5 − 2 = 3, 9 − 3 = 6, 7 − 5 = 2,
8 − 1 = 7;
12 − 6 = 6, 16 − 8 = 8, 14 − 5 = 9

Page 326

four, five; seven, eleven; nine, six;
ten, three; eight, two

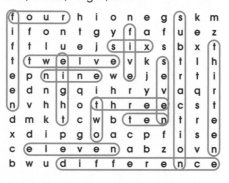

Page 327

7 + 2 = 9 − 4 = 5 − 3 = 2 + 9 = 11 + 5
= 16 − 8 = 8 + 4 = 12 + 6 = 18 − 9 =
9 + 1 = 10 + 4 = 14 − 8 = 6 + 2 = 8 +
3 = 11 − 3 = 8;
12 − 3 = 9 − 6 = 3 + 2 = 5 + 9 = 14 −
6 = 8 + 7 = 15 − 6 = 9 + 3 = 12 − 2 =
10 + 7 = 17 + 1 = 18 − 11 = 7 − 5 = 2 +
13 = 15 − 7 = 8 + 3 = 11

Page 328

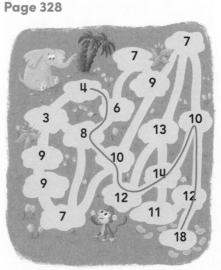

Page 329

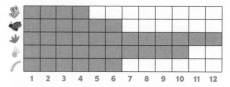

Page 330

1. First flower should be circled.
2. 6 + 10 = 16
3. 12 − 4 = 8
4. 4 + 6 = 10
5. 12 − 6 = 6
6. 4 + 10 = 14

Page 331

15 − 3 = 12, 6 + 7 = 13, 11 + 2 = 13,
17 − 4 = 13;
13 + 4 = 17, 18 − 3 = 15, 9 + 6 = 15,
15 + 2 = 17;
9 + 3 = 12, 8 + 3 = 11, 15 − 4 = 11,
18 − 7 = 11

Page 332

5 + 7 = 12, 8 + 3 = 11, 15 − 5 = 10,
18 − 9 = 9, 11 − 3 = 8, 12 − 5 = 7;
9 − 7 = 2, 12 − 8 = 4, 5 + 1 = 6,
16 − 8 = 8, 13 − 3 = 10, 7 + 5 = 12;
12 − 9 = 3, 11 − 5 = 6, 13 − 4 = 9,
7 + 6 = 13, 18 − 3 = 15, 11 + 7 = 18;
15 − 2 = 13, 4 + 7 = 11, 12 − 3 = 9,
12 − 5 = 7, 8 − 3 = 5, 12 − 9 = 3

Page 333
2, 4, 2;
3, 6, 4;
6, 4, 10

Page 334
5; 3 + 2 + 5 = 10; 4 + 5 + 7 = 16;
6; 7 + 2 = 9; 6 – 2 = 4;
5 + 3 + 2 + 6 + 2 + 3 = 21

Page 335
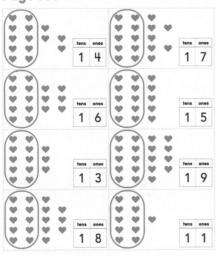

tens	ones
1	4

tens	ones
1	7

tens	ones
1	6

tens	ones
1	5

tens	ones
1	3

tens	ones
1	9

tens	ones
1	8

tens	ones
1	1

Page 336
4 tens 7 ones, 6 tens 4 ones;
7 tens 8 ones, 9 tens 6 ones

Page 337
34, 56, 42;
23, 65, 18;
91, 73, 68

Page 338
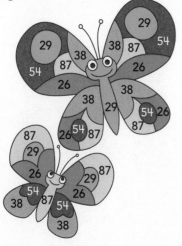

Page 339

	17	36	84	
78	29	59	14	48
88	24	35	66	98
18	43	77	38	88
78	65	56	46	26
	99	57	87	

Page 340
93 + 6 = 99, 82 + 4 = 86,
14 + 5 = 19, 21 + 7 = 28,
53 + 6 = 59;
45 + 4 = 49, 73 + 3 = 76,
36 + 3 = 39, 61 + 5 = 66,
32 + 7 = 39

Page 341
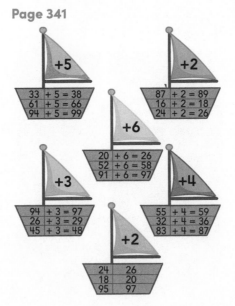

+5
33 + 5 = 38
61 + 5 = 66
94 + 5 = 99

+2
87 + 2 = 89
16 + 2 = 18
24 + 2 = 26

+6
20 + 6 = 26
52 + 6 = 58
91 + 6 = 97

+3
94 + 3 = 97
26 + 3 = 29
45 + 3 = 48

+4
55 + 4 = 59
32 + 4 = 36
83 + 4 = 87

+2
24   26
18   20
95   97

Page 342

Page 343
1. 39 – 7 = 32
2. 87 – 6 = 81
3. 25 – 4 = 21
4. 98 – 7 = 91
5. 54 – 1 = 53
6. 73 – 3 = 70
7. 42 – 2 = 40
8. 66 – 5 = 61

Page 344
42, 90, 76, 32, 82, 63, 81;
50, 35, 21, 21, 41, 90, 53;
30, 80, 20, 70, 60, 65, 74;
The box with 53 should be colored yellow. The box with 32 should be colored orange. The box with 74 should be colored red.

Page 345
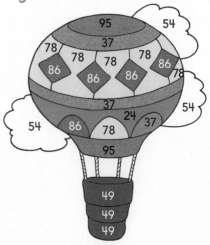

Page 346

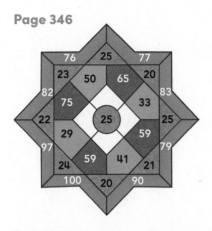

Page 347

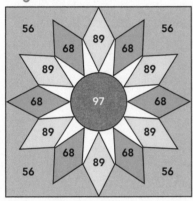

Page 348

Page 348 star illustration with numbers: 37, 58, 70, 42, 78, 87, 49, 86, 89, 59, 61, 86, 44, 42, 57

Page 349

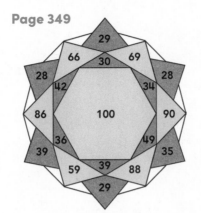

Page 350

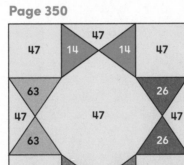

Page 351

39 – 12 = 27, 97 – 23 = 74,
59 – 18 = 41, 77 – 12 = 65;
79 – 52 = 27, 81 – 11 = 70,
88 – 46 = 42, 63 – 10 = 53;
58 – 43 = 15, 46 – 23 = 23,
35 – 24 = 11, 68 – 35 = 33;
32 – 12 = 20, 74 – 54 = 20,
69 – 54 = 15, 83 – 52 = 31

Page 352

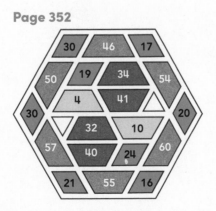

Page 353

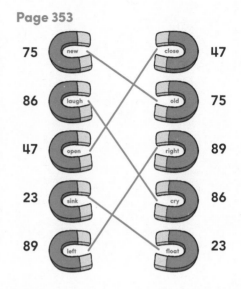

75 · new
86 · laugh
47 · open
23 · sink
89 · left
close · 47
old · 75
right · 89
cry · 86
float · 23

Page 354

34 + 13 = 47, 21 + 52 = 73,
47 + 10 = 57;
75 – 34 = 41, 62 – 21 = 41,
47 – 13 = 34

Page 355

38 + 24 = 62, 50 + 49 = 99,
56 + 25 = 81;
72 – 49 = 23, 56 – 24 = 32,
50 – 25 = 25

Page 356

1. Sunday
2. 89
3. Monday
4. 24
5. 79
6. 22

Page 357

34, 85, 26, 57; star;
71, 88, 42, 76, 85; light;
76, 63, 26, 85; heat;
71, 88, 13, 63; life

Page 358

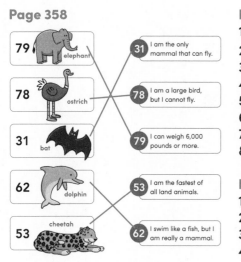

79 elephant	31 — I am the only mammal that can fly.
78 ostrich	78 — I am a large bird, but I cannot fly.
31 bat	79 — I can weigh 6,000 pounds or more.
62 dolphin	53 — I am the fastest of all land animals.
53 cheetah	62 — I swim like a fish, but I am really a mammal.

Page 359

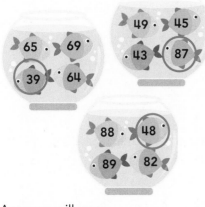

Answers will vary.

Page 360
Possible answers:
1. This is a pattern of three shapes, all the same color, that repeat.
2. This is a pattern of three shapes, each a different color, that repeat.
3. This is a pattern of three. All three are the same shape but are colored differently.
4. This is a pattern of sets of three numbers. The pattern continues by adding 1 to each of the three numbers.

Page 361
1. TSR, NML
2. ★, ◆
3. 50, 140
4. 72, 108
5. ✳, ■
6. df, pr
7. 26, 68
8. ←←, ↓↓

Page 362
1. 32, 42, 52, 62, 72, 82, 92
2. 70, 60, 50, 40, 30, 20, 10
3. 67, 57, 47, 37, 27, 17, 7
4. 44, 55, 66, 77, 88, 99

Page 363
1. Answers will vary.
2. Numbers will be colored in using an AB pattern of red and blue.

Page 364
Odd numbers: 1, 3, 5, 7
Even numbers: 4, 6, 8, 10

Page 365

Page 366
Estimates will vary.
2, 4, 6, 8, 10, 12, 14, 16, 18, 20;
5, 10, 15, 20

Page 367

	51	33	15	7	42	13
←	50	11	39	44	45	40
	25	48	46	52	38	19

13	29	35	47	3	1	36	49	43
53	18	20	31	45	7	17	34	5
16	14	49	22	5	23	3	51	32
37	41	12	7	24	26	28	30	55
54	10	11	27	31	1			
9	21	8	6	4	2	←		

Page 368

1	2	3	4	5	6	7	8	9	10
11	12	13	14	15	16	17	18	19	20
21	22	23	24	25	26	27	28	29	30
31	32	33	34	35	36	37	38	39	40
41	42	43	44	45	46	47	48	49	50
51	52	53	54	55	56	57	58	59	60
61	62	63	64	65	66	67	68	69	70
71	72	73	74	75	76	77	78	79	80
81	82	83	84	85	86	87	88	89	90
91	92	93	94	95	96	97	98	99	100

Answers will vary.

Page 369

20, 30, 40, 50, 60, 70, 80, 90

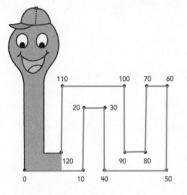

Page 370

Yield sign: triangle, 3
Caution sign: diamond, 4
Speed-limit sign: rectangle, 4
Stop sign: octagon, 8

Page 371

Left bird feeder: cube, octagon, hexagon, rectangle, square, rectangle solid
Right bird feeder : cylinder, triangle, circle, rectangle

Page 372

Diamond: 4 corners, 4 sides
Hexagon: 6 corners, 6 sides
Square: 4 corners, 4 sides
Triangle: 3 corners, 3 sides
Octagon: 8 corners, 8 sides
Rectangle: 4 corners, 4 sides

Page 373

Color the first butterfly, the second heart, the lightbulb, and the snowflake
Drawings should show the other halves.

Page 374

Color the circle, both squares, and the triangle.

Page 375

Drawings should show the other half of each shape.

Page 376

Patterns and equations will vary.

Page 377

15; 8

Page 378

Alex's coins: 25¢ + 25¢ + 10¢ = 60¢
Billy's coins: 10¢ + 10¢ + 10¢ + 10¢ + 10¢ + 5¢ + 5¢ + 1¢ + 1¢ + 1¢ = 63¢
63¢ > 60¢ Billy has more money.

Page 379

1¢: 11 coins for 11¢
5¢: 4 coins for 20¢
10¢: 3 coins for 30¢
25¢: 2 coins for 50¢

Page 380

Answers will vary.

Page 381

3 1/2 inches, 2 inches,
1 1/2 inches, 3 inches
Patty, Peter, Petunia, Paul

Page 382

pencil: 2
lunchbox: 1
crayon: 2
notebook: 1

Page 383

1 gallon = 4 quarts
1 quart = 2 pints
1 pint = 2 cups
1 cup = 12 tablespoons
1 tablespoon = 3 teaspoons

Page 384

1 + 2 + 1 + 2 = 6 inches
2 + 3 + 2 + 3 = 10 inches
2 + 5 + 2 + 5 = 14 inches

Page 385

book width: 2 centimeters
paper height: 3 centimeters
key: 4 centimeters
brush: 6 centimeters
5 cubes: 4 centimeters
10 cubes: 8 centimeters
shoe: 5 centimeters
hand: 3 centimeters

Page 386

Answers may vary. Check graph to make sure that it corresponds to the boxes checked.
chicken: see, hear, smell, touch
sun: see
milk: see, touch, taste
flowers: see, smell, touch
drums: see, hear, touch

Page 387

Answers will vary.

Page 388

1. (B, 9)
2. (F, 6)
3. (H, 10)
4. (D, 1)
5. (E, 8)
6. (C, 4)
7. (I, 5)
8. (G, 3)
9. (A, 7)
10. (J, 2)

Page 389

Page 390
Sunny days: 12
Cloudy days: 8
Rainy days: 5
Snowy days: 6
Sunny days

Page 391
Color shapes 1, 2, 5, 6, 7, and 8.

Page 392

Page 393

Page 394

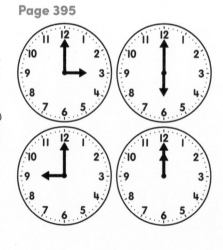

Page 395

Page 396

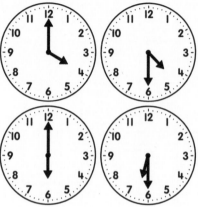

Page 397
Answers will vary.

Page 398

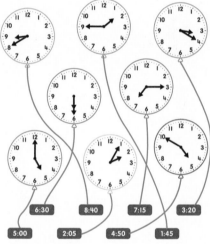

6:30   8:40   7:15   3:20

5:00   2:05   4:50   1:45

ALL ABOUT ME
BOOKLET

Draw or paste a picture of yourself here.

by

your name

Dear Family:
Welcome to the ALL ABOUT ME BOOKLET—starring your child! Read the prompts and work together to fill in the pages over time. TIP: If kids are pre-writers, feel free to dictate their responses while they draw the pictures. When the pages are complete, remove and staple them along the left-hand side. Voila! You and your child will have a literacy-boosting keepsake to read and treasure for many years to come.

Happy learning!
The Editors

CONTENTS

My Marvelous Name......................3

My Awesome Age.........................4

I'm a Star 5

My Hero! 6

Loved Ones................................7

Favorite Foods 8

Coolest Color.............................9

Amazing Animal.......................... 10

Best Book................................ 11

Kindness Cone........................... 12

When I Grow Up 13

Flower Facts 14

Celebration Song 15

Future Me 16

MY MARVELOUS NAME

My name begins with...
Circle the letter.

A B C D E F G
H I J K L M N O
P Q R S T U V W
X Y Z

Other words that begin with the same letter are...
Make a list.

_____

_____

_____

_____

_____
Write your first name on the line.

My name has this many letters...
Circle the number.

1 2 3 4 5 6 7 8
9 10 11 12 13
14 15 MORE

My name is special because...
Tell why.

_____

_____

MY AWESOME AGE

I'm this age!

Circle the number that shows your age.

HOORAY!

Circle that number of balloons.

Color that number of candles and write it in the circle.

I will wish for

_____

Write your wish.

I'M A STAR

Write eight things you like to do on the lines. Write one thing you like to say in the speech balloon.

1
2
3
4
5
6
7
8

MY HERO!

Write the name of your hero on the line.
Draw or paste a picture of his/her face on the circle.

_____

is my hero!

This person is my hero because....

_____

_____

LOVED ONES

Finish drawing the kid to make it look like you. Then write the names of the people and animals you love on the heart.

I love...

_____

_____

_____

_____

FAVORITE FOODS

Draw your favorite food on the plate and drink in the glass.

My VERY favorite food is _____.

My VERY favorite drink is _____.

Some other foods I like are _____

_____

8

COOLEST COLOR

Write the name of your favorite color on the crayon.
Make a picture using only that color.

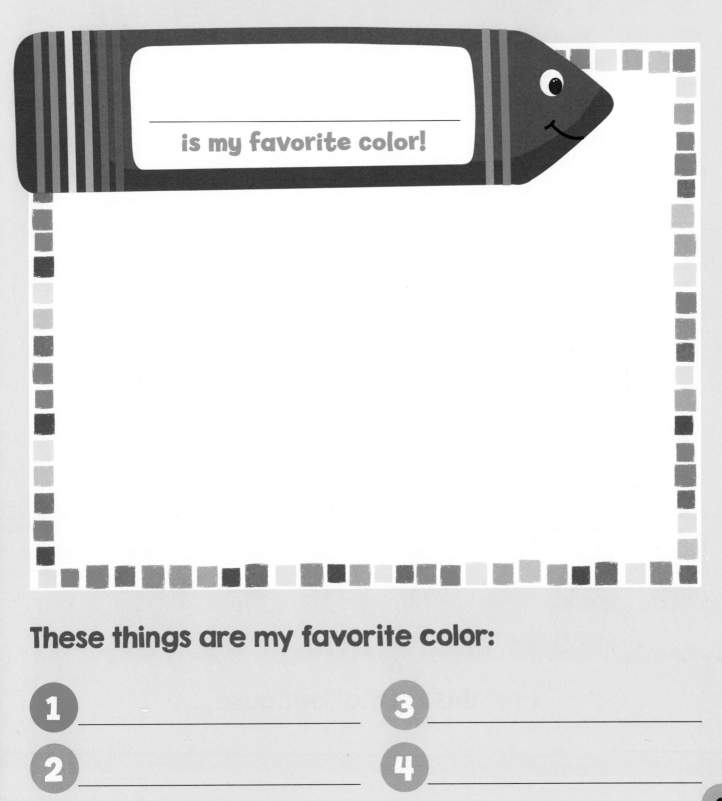

_____

is my favorite color!

These things are my favorite color:

1 _____

2 _____

3 _____

4 _____

AMAZING ANIMAL

Draw an animal you love in the frame. Write its name on the sign and the sound it makes in the speech balloon.

sound

My favorite animal:

_____

I ❤ this animal because...

_____.

BEST BOOK

Write the title and author of a favorite book. Then tell what it is about and rate it by shading in 1–5 stars.

Title

Author

This book is about _____

_____

_____.

I give it this many stars:

11

KINDNESS CONE

Complete the prompts to tell some special ways
you are sweet and kind.

A way I am kind to my family...

A way I am kind to my friends...

A way I am kind to my community...

Another way I am kind...

WHEN I GROW UP

Complete the prompts. Then draw yourself
dressed up for your dream job.

Something I might say on the job is:

When I grow up,
I want to be a/an:

_____
job

FLOWER FACTS

Fill in the leaves and petals to tell all about yourself.

hometown or city

nickname

family members

fun fact 2

friends

fun fact 1

first name

last name

CELEBRATION SONG

Fill in the blanks to write a special song about yourself.
Then sing it with your family and friends!

ALL-ABOUT-ME SONG

(Sung to the tune of "Happy Birthday")

I am _____.

name

That's true!

I am _____.

age

Yahoo!

I like _____ and

something you love

_____.

something else you love

I like _____, too!

something else you love

FUTURE ME

Draw your future self in the rocket window.
Then tell what you plan to do.

In the future I will...